SUM HOPE

SUM HOPE

Breaking the Numbers Barrier

STEVE CHINN

LONDON NEW YORK SYDNEY TORONTO

This edition published 1999 BCA
By arrangement with Souvenir Press Ltd

CN 3043

Copyright © 1998 by Steve Chinn

The right of Steve Chinn to be identified as author
of this work has been asserted by him in accordance with
the Copyright, Designs and Patents Act 1988.

First published 1998 by
Souvenir Press Ltd,
43 Great Russell Street, London WC1B 3PA

Typeset by Rowland Phototypesetting Ltd, Bury St Edmunds, Suffolk
Printed in Great Britain by Clays Ltd, St Ives plc

This book is written to help you do maths
with more confidence and success

Contents

Introduction

Please read this first

Maths, usually in the shape of numbers, causes levels of anxiety and denial ('I never was any good at maths') way beyond any other school subject. Yet the need to use maths lingers after schooling has finished, it is part of our everyday life—for example, we have to use money, we deal with time, we meet percentages.

This book does not attempt to reteach all the maths you didn't learn at school, nor should it. I think that most people know more maths than they realise, so I have tried to clarify and pull together those vague, half-remembered, half-understood ideas.

I have tackled some of the areas of maths that are most needed in life, at the same time trying to give you an understanding of the basic ideas of numeracy. I have attempted to give simple explanations, but you will still need to involve yourself in the learning process and persevere . . . all will become clear as you go through the book.

I have long recognised that not everyone uses or relates to the same methods of doing mathematics. Throughout the book I have tried to explain alternative ways. No one method is preferable to any other, but a particular one might suit you better. The only way you will know is to give them all a proper try and then choose the one that works best for you. The different methods may help you to form a better understanding of maths processes.

Many of the ideas in maths crop up again and again, often in different disguises. This has a minus and a plus effect. The minus effect is that if you do not understand the idea, you will probably fail to understand it each time it is used. The plus effect is that if you can get even some understanding of the idea, then each extra time it occurs you should use the new experience to strengthen your understanding. I have tried to focus on this plus!

Remember that maths is a skill, just like basketball or tennis. If you don't practise the skill it will fade. So, if the ideas in this book help you, they may still need, at some stage in the future, a little top-up work (revision), especially if you are not using the maths regularly. As with many skills, learning is often most effective as 'little and often'.

There is also, in the Appendix, a list of other books in case you get hooked and want to learn more.

1 What can Cause Problems with Learning Maths?

If you can't do mathematics it is likely to be for some very good reasons, which probably have little to do with how clever you are. There are many factors that can get in the way of learning mathematics. Some of these are discussed below and you may recognise several as relevant to you. You may be unlucky enough to be affected by all of them, but even then you may have found ways of getting round some or most of the difficulties they create. If you haven't, this book will help you to find some ways.

You may have reached the stage where you have decided that enough is enough and that you and mathematics can live without each other. I hope to persuade you to have one more try. It is a useful skill in so many aspects of life.

When you have a problem, a good starting point is to try to understand what caused it. This often helps you understand the problem itself and should make it easier to tackle. This awareness may even help you to avoid or at least reduce the influence of such problems in the future.

So, let's look at these problem factors . . .

ANXIETY

Anxiety can really get in the way of learning.

It is a cumulation, a consequence of all the other factors and difficulties, of the way they have affected your attempts to succeed in mathematics, and how they have affected your attitude towards carrying on working at this subject.

Anxiety is the last difficulty to occur (because it is a

consequence of all the other problems) and the first to overcome if you are to return to using mathematics and numbers.

One of the best ways to reduce this anxiety is to find some areas of success. It is important to know that everyone can do *some* maths. As my colleague Richard Ashcroft says, mathematics is a subject that builds like a wall, but it is a wall that can still stand and be strong with some gaps, some missing bricks. You do not have to be perfect in *all* of maths to have success. For example, an ex-student of mine still cannot given an instant answer to 'What is 8 × 7?' but he does now have a degree . . . in maths.

The work in this book will attempt to use and build on what you know.

To be good, or even just OK, at mathematics you have to practise, but if you are anxious about it you will probably try to avoid doing any practice at all! For you to feel more comfortable and then, hopefully, confident, I have to persuade you to change your mind and try some practice.

If you do suffer from maths anxiety you are certainly not alone (see, for example, p.151). Whole books have been written on this subject. My guess is that the mathematically anxious are in the majority!

DO TRY THE IDEAS IN THIS BOOK.
THEY ARE DESIGNED TO HELP YOU SUCCEED
AND START TO OVERCOME SOME OF THAT ANXIETY.

Learning how to do maths successfully will help reduce anxiety. Set your own targets and your own speed of working. Make both of these realistic, and then slowly increase your goals. Above all . . . BEGIN.

MEMORY

One of the most common problems in mathematics is remembering the basic facts of numeracy, in particular the times table facts (such as 6 × 7 and 4 × 9). Some people find this task virtually impossible. And since this is one of the first demands from teachers of mathematics it can create an early sense of failure and inadequacy.

Memory can also let you down when learning addition and subtraction facts (such as 7 + 8 and 13 – 6), but these can often be worked out quite quickly on your fingers. These times table and addition facts are the basic building-blocks of number work, but if you cannot remember them all is not lost: there are some ideas to help (see chapter 3). Many of the suggestions in this book try to pull together the number facts and methods, so that they become mutually supportive.

Your memory may also let you down when you try to recall a process or method, such as how to work out percentages. I shall try to make each process real by relating it to something you know, to give you a good understanding and add some meaning to the maths.

If someone asks you to recall a fact from memory, say a times table fact, and your memory is a blank, it is something like looking into a deep, black pit. There seems to be no way out, and if remembering the fact is your only option, then there *is* no way out. I shall try to provide some steps to bring you out of the pit.

Doing sums 'in your head' (mental arithmetic) can overload your memory, so I have included some suggestions to reduce the possibility of this problem occurring and help you tackle this activity.

Some methods for doing arithmetic are best when written, some are better to use 'in your head'. One of the reasons for memory overload is that people try to use written methods for mental arithmetic and not all written methods transfer to being done in the head. I shall attempt to suggest which methods are better to use for each case.

Any memory decays or slips away. What holds it in your mind is frequent reminding. The more you see, hear, say or feel (putting a memory into the brain by all senses) an experience, the firmer is its permanence in your mind.

WORDS

Sometimes the words people use when talking about arithmetic are confusing. I have a similar problem when a fluent
computer expert starts explaining new software to me. It
seems to me that they have a language of their own (which, of
course, they do!).

One source of possible confusion in our early experience of
maths is that we use more than one word for a particular
mathematics meaning—for example, adding can be: 6 *more*
than 3, 17 *and* 26, 52 *plus* 39, 15 *add* 8.

Sometimes the words we use have other, non-mathematical
meanings—for example, 30 *take away* 12, 18 *shared* between 3
people.

Sometimes the same words can mean two things—for
example, 'What is 5 *more than* 8?' is *addition*, but 'Emily has
16 sweets. She has 6 *more than* Sarah. How many sweets does
Sarah have?' is *subtraction*.

Sometimes the words for the more common, everyday
examples of mathematics ideas do not fit the normal pattern
of other maths vocabulary. For example, with fractions we
have special names for the two most common values which we
call one half and one quarter rather than one second and one
fourth (which would fit better into the fraction pattern). The
other fractions use words that are better related to the
numbers in the fractions, such as one third ($\frac{1}{3}$), one seventh ($\frac{1}{7}$)
and one twentieth ($\frac{1}{20}$).

The 'teen' numbers are another case of a break with the
normal pattern causing possible confusion, especially for
young children. The way we say the teen numbers is backwards to numbers in the twenties, thirties, forties and other
two-figure numbers. So we say eighteen (eight ten) and write
18, whereas we say twenty-eight, which has the figures in the
correct word order 28. This particular situation is exacerbated
by the words eleven (which could be oneteen) and twelve
(which could be twoteen) and hindered by the words thirteen
(threeteen) and fifteen (fiveteen). I suppose a small benefit of
eleven and twelve is that they save two more teenage years.

Although these examples may sound simple, they can be enough to start an impression in the learner that maths is confusing.

SEQUENCES AND PATTERNS

Sequences and patterns such as 2, 4, 6, 8, 10, 12 . . . or 10, 20, 30, 40, 50, 60 . . . are very much a part of maths. You need to be able to remember them and often to adapt them. So 10, 20, 30, 40 . . . can be adapted to 13, 23, 33, 43, 53 . . . Some people find this adaptation difficult.

If you can remember and recognise sequences and patterns it will help your memory. For example, it is much easier to remember the seven numbers 1234567 than a random set such as 5274318.

This book will show you lots of suggestions and ideas for organising and accessing facts.

SPEED

Not only do people expect you to do maths correctly, they often expect you to do it quickly. Trying to work more quickly than you naturally do will increase the pressure on you and will almost certainly make you less successful. This is like taking up jogging. You cannot convert yourself from a couch potato to a four-minute-mile runner overnight (and you may never ever reach that four-minute goal, nor want to!). If you do want to start jogging, or squash, or oil painting or fishing, you will need to learn new skills and practise them. As you practise you get faster and the task gets easier or, to be precise, because the task stays the same you find it easier. Then you can try to add in more skills.

You can develop quicker ways with maths, but on the whole this is very much a secondary goal, unless you want to appear on *Countdown*.

THINKING STYLE

It seems obvious that not everyone thinks the same way. We each have our own thinking style for all the different things we do in life. This includes having our own thinking style for maths.

Our thinking style (or cognitive style) is the way we work out maths problems. It is possible to simplify this individuality down a little and imagine that our own thinking style lies somewhere along a line or a spectrum. At one end of this spectrum are the *inchworms* and at the other end are the *grasshoppers*.

An inchworm likes to work with formulas and set methods. Inchworms work step by step, preferring to write things down. They see the details. They also tend to see numbers exactly as they are written—a sort of numerical equivalent of a literal interpretation.

A grasshopper often goes straight to an answer. Grasshoppers rarely write down while working out. They like to see the whole picture—they overview. They are intuitive and can be confused by formulas. They tend to see a broad value in numbers, interrelating them to comfortable values—for example, 97 is seen as a 'bit less than' 100.

If someone tries to explain a grasshopper method to an inchworm, the inchworm learner will probably not relate to the method. And vice versa.

For example, an inchworm will add 340 and 97 step by step, starting with the units—that is 0 add 7, then 4 add 9 and finally 3 add (the carried) 1 to give an answer of 437. Inchworm workers usually like to use pen and paper to write down their method, probably as:

$$
\begin{array}{r}
340 \\
+\ 97 \\
\hline
437 \\
\end{array}
$$

Faced with the same question, a grasshopper will look at the 97 and round it up to 100, add 340 and 100 and subtract the 3 (which made 97 into 100), getting an answer of 437 without writing anything down.

It is best if you can learn how to make use of both thinking styles.

Generally speaking, grasshoppers are better at mental arithmetic and estimating, while inchworms are good at using formulas and detailed work. So you can see that to be versatile in your maths skills you need to be able to draw on both styles of thinking.

Some people are set at the extremes of the style spectrum and find it very hard to adjust to the other style. If you were one of these grasshopper pupils being taught by an extreme inchworm teacher, you may well have found that communication between you was difficult (and, of course, so did your teacher).

Throughout this book you will see that some methods are more inchworm-friendly and some are more grasshopper-friendly. It may well be your thinking style that makes some methods easier to understand than others.

Remember, both thinking styles have strengths and weaknesses. You need to learn the best of both.

ATTITUDE

This is closely linked to anxiety and is a good final topic for this chapter.

One of the attitudes adopted by people who are not succeeding in maths is that of not caring, not trying. This is usually based on an idea of protecting yourself from being wrong, from failing (which any sensible person tries to avoid). So if you do not try to answer a question you cannot get it wrong. But this also means that by not allowing yourself to be wrong you are not allowing yourself to learn. I hope to encourage you to take the risk of sometimes being wrong.

One of the key factors for success is a willingness to take a risk. If you look at every number problem and think, 'I can't even begin that,' then you will not learn. You need to practise and experience new ideas.

Often in schools children are placed in situations where they are asked a question to which they do not know the answer. Rather than be wrong, they do not try to work it out. They are withdrawing from a learning opportunity . . . understandably.

So . . .

You have to be involved in the learning. Learning is not a 'sit back and hope for something to happen' activity. This book will help you learn some new ways of doing maths, but only if you practise the ideas. I wish I could provide a magic learning pill which you could take each day to give you instant knowledge and understanding, but I can't. The magic only comes from a combination of (hopefully) good explanations by the teacher and a willingness by the learner to practise and take risks.

2   Understanding Numbers
(and how to write cheques)

When we *write* numbers they are made up of different combinations of just ten symbols or figures. These are:

$$1, 2, 3, 4, 5, 6, 7, 8, 9 \text{ and } 0$$

Our numbers are based on tens. It is no coincidence that we have ten fingers!

To explain how written numbers are built up I shall use an example which shows how you count to, and write, one hundred and eleven as 111.

Imagine you have a job as a sheep counter and that you are counting a large number of sheep (and still staying awake). You can count up to the first nine sheep by using your fingers and writing the numbers with one number symbol or figure, for example 6. When you get to ten you can start again counting the next ten on your fingers, but you call in your first assistant sheep counter to record that you have one ten already counted. You ask your assistant sheep counter to use one finger to represent the one ten you have just counted. This is bringing in a second number symbol or figure. Let's say you have counted sixteen sheep, then you can use two of the number symbols or figures to write this down as:

16

(for the first ten you counted)   (for the next 6 you counted)

We can use the ten number symbols written together (in an order which also tells us about the value of the number) to represent any number of sheep. For example, forty-four sheep is written as:

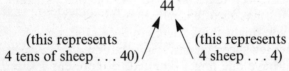

44

(this represents   (this represents
4 tens of sheep . . . 40)   4 sheep . . . 4)

So the first 4 you write represents 4 tens (40) and the second 4 represents 4 units (4).

Imagine now that you have counted ninety-nine sheep. Your assistant has nine fingers counted and you also have nine fingers counted. This writes up as

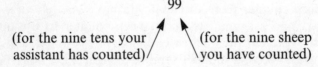

99

(for the nine tens your   (for the nine sheep
assistant has counted)   you have counted)

The first 9 you write represents 9 tens (90) and the second 9 represents 9 units (9).

Now, think what happens to the counting when the next sheep after number 99 appears. You reach another ten on your fingers and your assistant sheep counter also reaches ten (but his are ten lots of ten). You now need to bring in the second assistant sheep counter to count one finger (which represents 1 hundred or ten lots of ten).

This number, one hundred, is written as 100. Now we are using three symbols, 1 and 0 and 0. The second assistant sheep counter's fingers count the hundreds, which are ten lots of ten.

The next sheep takes us to 101, so the first assistant sheep counter still has zero tens to count. However, you need him there or you might think there are only 11 sheep.

Another ten sheep take us to one hundred and eleven sheep, 111. You have one finger counted to represent 1 sheep. The first assistant sheep counter has one finger counted to represent 1 ten sheep and the second assistant sheep counter has one finger counted to represent 1 hundred sheep.

So in 111, each 1 represents a different value:

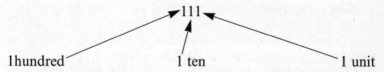

You have used three figures to represent the number one hundred and eleven. In this particular number all three figures are 1, but each 1 represents a different amount: 1 hundred, 1 ten and 1 unit.

This is the way all numbers are built up and written. So when you get to thousands you bring in a fourth number symbol or figures—for example:

five thousand, six hundred and eighty-nine is

5 689

Note that this thousands number is written with a gap between the thousands figure and the hundreds figure. This is a convention designed to help you visually organise the figures in a large number. Another gap is introduced between the millions figure and the hundred thousands figure.

The next group uses five number symbols, for example:

twenty-three thousand, four hundred and sixty-seven is

23 467

Then six-figure numbers, for example:

nine hundred and fifty-four thousand, seven hundred and eighty-one is

954 781

And on to a million, a seven-figure number, for example:

three million, two hundred and fifty-six thousand, nine hundred and forty-two is

3 256 942

Mathematicians talk about the *place value* of numbers. What they mean is that the value of a particular figure in a number depends on its place (or position) within that number. So, in the number above, 3 256 942, there are two 2s. The 2 between the 3 and the 5 represents 200 000 (two hundred thousand), and the 2 at the right-hand end represents just 2 (two units). So the place value of the same figure can be very different!

The most common problem with writing a number in figures from a number in words occurs when there are zeros in the number. In the million number example above there was a figure for every place value. Look back at p.21 and the number one hundred and one. There are only two number words but you need three figures to write the number 101. The zero is needed to show that the number is more than 100. Without the zero the number is 11.

Try a slightly harder example: four thousand and sixty-five . . . 4 065. There are three word numbers (four, sixty and five), but it is a four-figure number. The zero is used because there are zero (no) hundreds. Without the zero, the number becomes four hundred and sixty-five . . . 465.

Go harder again: five hundred thousand and six . . . 500 006. There are two word numbers (five and six) for a six-figure number. Without the zeros this big number becomes 56!

How to write word numbers in figures (useful for cheques)
Businesses often have special cheques for big sums of money (where mistakes can be expensive).

This gives a good strategy for writing numbers as figures. Work to a place value grid:

million	hundred thousand	ten thousand	thousand	hundred	ten	unit

Take the number and read it, for example:

seven million, four thousand and ten
(just in case you win the Lottery)

It says seven million, so put 7 in the million slot.

million	hundred thousand	ten thousand	thousand	hundred	ten	unit
7						

It says four thousand, so put 4 in the thousand slot.

million	hundred thousand	ten thousand	thousand	hundred	ten	unit
7			4			

It says ten, so put 1 in the ten slot.

million	hundred thousand	ten thousand	thousand	hundred	ten	unit
7			4		1	

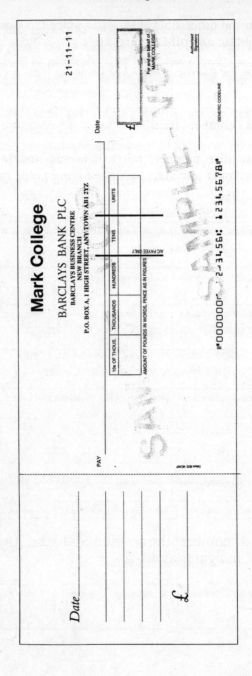

Now fill in the other slots with zeros, since the word number did not contain any other figures.

million	hundred thousand	ten thousand	thousand	hundred	ten	unit
7	0	0	4	0	1	0

The word number translates to a seven-figure number, 7 004 010.

Try a smaller number, **thirty thousand and twenty-four**. Read the number and start to fill in a place value grid.

Thirty thousand . . .

million	hundred thousand	ten thousand	thousand	hundred	ten	unit
		3				

and twenty . . .

million	hundred thousand	ten thousand	thousand	hundred	ten	unit
		3			2	

four . . .

million	hundred thousand	ten thousand	thousand	hundred	ten	unit
		3			2	4

Fill in the zeros . . .

million	hundred thousand	ten thousand	thousand	hundred	ten	unit
		3	0	0	2	4

The word number thirty thousand and twenty-four writes out in figures as 30 024.

A WAY OF CHECKING YOUR ANSWER

There is a basic check you can make on whether or not you
have written a number correctly. You count the number of
figures in the number.

Sometimes you read in newspapers of people receiving a
five-figure or six-figure salary. The number of figures in a
number gives some idea of the value of the number. So, the
first (and lowest) five-figure number is 10 000 and the last (and
biggest) is 99 999 . . . quite a big range!

The first six-figure number is 100 000 and the last is 999 999
(one short of a million).

Hundreds are three-figure numbers.
Thousands are four-figure numbers.
Ten thousands are five-figure numbers.
Hundred thousands are six-figure numbers.
Millions are seven-figure numbers.
Billions are ten-figure numbers.
Trillions are thirteen-figure numbers.

3 The Basic Building-Blocks of Maths (addition and times table facts)

If you can learn the basic facts such as $6 + 7 = 13$, $13 - 6 = 7$, $5 \times 6 = 30$, $30 \div 5 = 6$ and recall them quickly, it will obviously be a big help when working with numbers. If you can't learn them, I have given in this chapter some suggestions you can try to help you. There are also some suggestions to help you work out the facts you can't remember (strategies), and if that still doesn't do the trick then many of the methods for doing number work described later in this book go round the problem.

It is better if you can get to these basic number facts quickly, either by direct memory or by efficient strategies. You have to decide what is best for you. The time you spend on this task must be rewarding in terms of success or you will simply lose interest in the work. With any topic in this book, never be afraid to move on for a while and then return for another try. Sometimes knowing something about the work ahead helps you understand the earlier work.

ADDITION AND SUBTRACTION FACTS

These are the basic facts, from $0 + 0$ to $10 + 10$ and $20 - 10$ to $0 - 0$.

They are called basic because they are the basis of all additions and subtractions. So if you know that $3 + 8 = 11$, you will see this used again and again in any example involving 8 added to 3, such as:

$$3 + 8 = 11 \qquad 3 + 18 = 21$$
$$13 + 8 = 21 \qquad 13 + 28 = 41$$
$$23 + 18 = 41 \qquad 300 + 800 = 1100$$
$$30 + 80 = 110$$

This pattern is very useful. What it means, in effect, is that you can develop a knowledge of one fact into many other examples.

One of the ways you can help yourself understand maths is to use objects with which you are familiar to illustrate an idea. Coins are a good example.

Numbers use place value (p.22). A figure can be used as a unit or a ten or a hundred and so on. For example, 2 is 2 units. The 2 in 20 is 2 tens and the 2 in 200 is 2 hundreds. Money is a good visual support since one pence coins count as units, ten pence coins count as tens and one pound coins count as hundreds.

£2   20p   2p

Try the first two examples (3 + 8 and 13 + 8) with money. Set up the basic fact first. Take 3 one pence coins and add them to 8 one pence coins. Count them to show 11 one pence coins. You could exchange (or trade) 10 of the one pence coins for 1 ten pence coin.

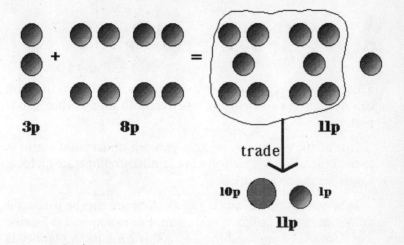

So adding 8 to 3 gives 1 ten and 1 unit.
Now try 13 + 8 with coins.

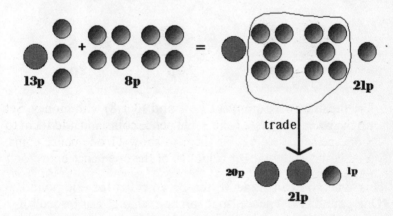

Put together the coins. This gives you 1 ten pence coin and 11 one pence coins. Trade 10 of the one pence coins for 1 ten pence coin. You now have 2 ten pence coins and 1 one pence coin, which is 21 pence. This is the same sum as the basic fact, except you started with an extra ten pence coin.

Try 3 + 18 with coins.

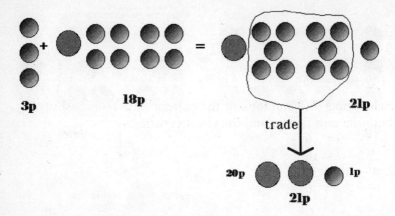

3p   18p   21p

trade

20p   21p   1p

Now try 30 + 80 with ten pence coins.

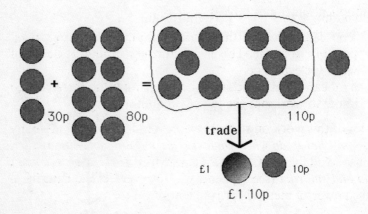

30p   80p   110p

trade

£1   10p

£1.10p

This time you can trade 10 ten pence coins for one pound. (One pound is 100 pence, so it can be exchanged or traded for 10 lots of 10 pence, which is also 100 pence.)

In each example you were following the same procedure. This is one of the strengths of maths—you can always build on what you know to extend what you know.

Other examples:

Adding 9 (look at the patterns, in both the unit figures and the tens figures):

$9 + 6 = 15$
$19 + 6 = 25$
$9 + 16 = 25$
$29 + 16 = 45$
$49 + 36 = 85$

Subtracting 9 (again look at the patterns and relationships in both the unit figures and the tens figures):

$15 - 9 = 6$
$25 - 9 = 16$
$45 - 19 = 26$
$85 - 39 = 46$

Back to the basics
There are two ways to access the basic facts of addition and multiplication (times tables):

1 You can memorise them, for example by chanting them, possibly to music. This is called rote learning. It does not work for everyone.
2 You can learn some strategies which use the facts you do know to work out the facts you do not know.

A lot of this work on strategies is covered in great detail in my books *What to do when you can't learn the times tables* (which is also available on CD-ROM) and *What to do when you can't add and subtract* (see Appendix). However, let me describe a very powerful method for rote learning.

If you are trying to remember a phone number while you look for a pen and paper to write it down, you will probably keep repeating it under your breath. This is sub-vocalising and is the basis of a learning technique called *self-voice echo*. Apparently we learn best from our own voice, hence self voice-echo. Some years ago now I tested this out on some teenage boys who knew very few times table facts, comparing self-voice echo with some other rote-learning techniques. The self-voice group made the best gains, but even in that group there was one boy who did not make any gain . . . so, the best way to find out if it will work for you is to give a try.

You need a tape-recorder and the facts you want to learn written clearly on a sheet of paper, preferably a few (say five) at one time. Record the five facts onto tape, leaving a four- or five-second gap between each fact. Now use the play and replay buttons on the tape-player to echo back one fact several times. It is usually better to use headphones. It is important to look at the fact as you say it, because then you are pushing the fact into your brain by seeing, listening and, if you are mouthing, muttering the fact as you hear yourself saying it—in other words, sub-vocalising. This multisensory input helps learning.

Practise about five facts at each session. Make a session fairly short as this is a method which is quite demanding on your perseverance levels. Only by trying it will you find out if it works for you.

Relating the basic facts

In my experience, most people know at least some maths, often more than they realise. This applies to the basic addition facts. There are 121 basic facts. Of these, only a small number cause difficulty, so the learning task is not 121, but more likely to be about 25 facts.

+	0	1	2	3	4	5	6	7	8	9	10
0	0	1	2	3	4	5	6	7	8	9	10
1	1	2	3	4	5	6	7	8	9	10	11
2	2	3	4	5	6	7	8	9	10	11	12
3	3	4	5	6	7	8	9	10	11	12	13
4	4	5	6	7	8	9	10	11	12	13	14
5	5	6	7	8	9	10	11	12	13	14	15
6	6	7	8	9	10	11	12	13	14	15	16
7	7	8	9	10	11	12	13	14	15	16	17
8	8	9	10	11	12	13	14	15	16	17	18
9	9	10	11	12	13	14	15	16	17	18	19
10	10	11	12	13	14	15	16	17	18	19	20

One of the key ideas in this book is to build on the facts and knowledge you already have and thus develop it. The addition facts are a good example of this. They also illustrate the idea of finding the 'easy' number and 'easy' fact within the 'hard' numbers and 'hard' facts. Building on what you know is a good way to learn. Let's look at two examples of this idea:

One of the addition facts which is usually known is 5 + 5 = 10

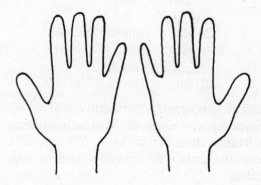

First, add on one more to make 5 + 5 into 5 + 5 + 1 which gives an answer of 11. So 5 + 5 has become 5 + 6 (or 6 + 5):

$$5 + 6 = 11 \qquad \text{and} \qquad 6 + 5 = 11$$

Now, a second extension of 5 + 5. Return to 5 + 5 and move 1 from the first 5 to the second 5. This keeps the answer as 10, but now the two numbers adding to make 10 are:

$$4 + 6 = 10 \qquad \text{and} \qquad 6 + 4 = 10$$

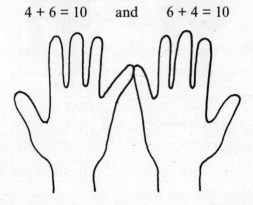

These two manoeuvres have extended the one fact, $5 + 5 =$ 10, into four more facts. The other 'doubles' can be treated the same.

For the second example, adding 9, start with the easy addition pattern of adding on to 10, for example:

$$10 + 1 = 11$$
$$10 + 2 = 12$$
$$10 + 3 = 13$$
$$10 + 4 = 14$$
$$10 + 5 = 15$$
$$10 + 6 = 16$$

Now, relate 9 to 10 . . . 9 is less than 10, so comparing the addition fact of 9 plus 6 to the addition of 10 plus 6, the answer must be 1 less. This gives a second step in the calculation, that of subtracting 1:

$$17 - 1 = 16$$

For some people, adding 9 is one hard step. But adding 9 can be done instead by using two easy steps.

Step 1: Add 10.
Step 2: Subtract 1.

9 is the hard number, 10 and 1 are the easy numbers, used instead of 9.

These two ideas can be used for several facts . . . 28 facts can be derived from 7 facts:

2 + 2 = 4	2 + 3 = 5	3 + 2 = 5	1 + 3 = 4	3 + 1 = 4
3 + 3 = 6	3 + 4 = 7	4 + 3 = 7	2 + 4 = 6	4 + 2 = 6
4 + 4 = 8	4 + 5 = 9	5 + 4 = 9	3 + 5 = 8	5 + 3 = 8
5 + 5 = 10	5 + 6 = 11	6 + 5 = 11	4 + 6 = 10	6 + 4 = 10
6 + 6 = 12	6 + 7 = 13	7 + 6 = 13	5 + 7 = 12	7 + 5 = 12
7 + 7 = 14	7 + 8 = 15	8 + 7 = 15	6 + 8 = 14	8 + 6 = 14
8 + 8 = 16	8 + 9 = 17	9 + 8 = 17	7 + 9 = 16	9 + 7 = 16

Adding 9 by using adding 10 and subtracting 1 is a 'two easy steps for one hard step' strategy. Adding 8 can be done by a similar idea. Since 8 is 10 take away 2, adding 8 can be done by adding 10 and subtracting 2.

So, 14 facts are derived from 7 facts.

3 + 10 = 13	3 + 9 = 12	3 + 8 = 11
4 + 10 = 14	4 + 9 = 13	4 + 8 = 12
5 + 10 = 15	5 + 9 = 14	5 + 8 = 13
6 + 10 = 16	6 + 9 = 15	6 + 8 = 14
7 + 10 = 17	7 + 9 = 16	7 + 8 = 15
8 + 10 = 18	8 + 9 = 17	8 + 8 = 16
9 + 10 = 19	9 + 9 = 18	9 + 8 = 17

These simple strategies have mopped up most of the difficult addition facts. If you want to make them even clearer, try using money to show how they work. For example, adding 8 + 4 via 10 + 4:

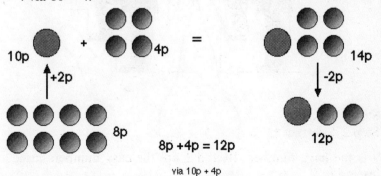

10p + 4p = 14p

+2p

-2p

8p

8p + 4p = 12p

12p

via 10p + 4p

A collection of addition facts which can be really useful is the collection which mathematicians call the number bonds for 10. These are the pairs of numbers which add to make 10. They start with 10 + 0 and then follow a pattern through 5 + 5 to 0 + 10.

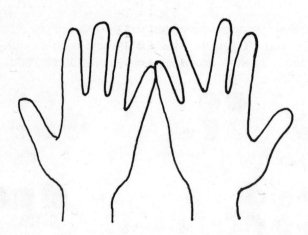

Another way to picture the number bonds for 10 is to use the ten fingers on your hands. As you move your fingers over, one at a time, you move through the number bonds for ten.

TIMES TABLE FACTS

Recently I spoke to a very intelligent young woman who is studying maths at A level. She has been offered a place at Oxford University to study engineering. We were talking about her difficulties with some areas of maths and she recalled with great feeling and self-awareness her experiences, as a seven-year-old, of being unable to commit the times tables to memory. All the children in the class who succeeded at this task received a special badge. She didn't, and although now she can look back and see that this seems trivial, at the time it had an enormous effect on her self-image of her ability to do maths. *Sadly this story is not unique.*

There are 121 times table facts, which can be presented as the traditional columns or tables—for example, the four times table:

$$1 \times 4 = 4$$
$$2 \times 4 = 8$$
$$3 \times 4 = 12$$
$$4 \times 4 = 16$$
$$5 \times 4 = 20$$
$$6 \times 4 = 24$$
$$7 \times 4 = 28$$
$$8 \times 4 = 32$$
$$9 \times 4 = 36$$
$$10 \times 4 = 40$$

The times table facts can also be shown, altogether, in a table square:

×	0	1	2	3	4	5	6	7	8	9	10
0	0	0	0	0	0	0	0	0	0	0	0
1	0	1	2	3	4	5	6	7	8	9	10
2	0	2	4	6	8	10	12	14	16	18	20
3	0	3	6	9	12	15	18	21	24	27	30
4	0	4	8	12	16	20	24	28	32	36	40
5	0	5	10	15	20	25	30	35	40	45	50
6	0	6	12	18	24	30	36	42	48	54	60
7	0	7	14	21	28	35	42	49	56	63	70
8	0	8	16	24	32	40	48	56	64	72	80
9	0	9	18	27	36	45	54	63	72	81	90
10	0	10	20	30	40	50	60	70	80	90	100

Again, it is my experience that very few people know absolutely none of these facts. Whatever your own feelings of achievement or otherwise in mathematics, you will have learned at least some of these facts, usually the tables with the best patterns, that is the 0×, 1×, 2×, 5× and 10×. Surprisingly, if you use the table square as the way the facts are presented rather than the separate times tables, this leaves only 36 facts to learn. Later on I shall show you how to reduce these 36 with very little effort.

The reason why these 121 facts reduce to 36 is that each of those easy tables contains some of the facts from the harder tables. For example, from the seven times table these facts are: 0×7, 1×7, 2×7, 5×7 and 10×7.

The number of remaining facts on the table square is reduced even further by a useful maths idea—that you get the same answer to a multiplication of two numbers irrespective of which multiplies which. For example, 6×8 and 8×6 both give 48 and 3×4 and 4×3 both give 12. *(This idea will be used again when I explain how to add and subtract fractions.)*

To explain this, try setting out 3 × 4 in 1p coins:

Describing what you have depends on whether you look at rows or columns. There are 4 rows of 3 or 3 columns of 4. Both are 12.

The toughest fact in the times table is generally considered to be 7 × 8 (and the same fact in its 8 × 7 form). This particular fact is one of only two to follow a special pattern:

$$5\ 6\ 7\ 8$$

becomes

$$56 = 7 \times 8$$

The other fact is 3 × 4 = 12:

$$1\ 2\ 3\ 4$$

becomes

$$12 = 3 \times 4$$

The easy steps strategy
The remaining missing facts can be treated by the same idea we used for addition facts—to use what you know to make one hard step into two easy steps. That is, relate the numbers, particularly by finding the 'easy' numbers in the harder numbers.

I shall also introduce you to the link between multiplication and addition, since this is one basis of the two easy steps methods.

Multiplication is the repeated addition of the same number. A times table fact such as 3 × 8 is the repeated addition 8 + 8 + 8 = 24:

3 × 8 is   (8
            8
          +8

This addition can be done one step at a time, but it is also easy to group the numbers as shown, that is 2 × 8 and 1 × 8.

So 3 × 8 is 2 × 8 (= 16) plus one more 8, that is 24.

Another example:

6 × 4 is   /   4
          (4
          (4
          (4
           \   4
             +4

The 4s can be added one at a time or grouped into five 4s and one 4 as shown. This makes 6 × 4 into two easier steps:

5 × 4 = 20 and 1 × 4 = 4

so 6 × 4 = 24   5 × 4 = 20
                     1 × 4 = 4

6 times 4 is 5 × 4 (= 20) plus one more 4, that is 24.

This strategy looks for the easy numbers within the harder number. For times tables:

A 3× fact is calculated as a 2× fact plus a 1× fact (2 + 1 = 3).
A 6× fact is calculated as a 5× fact plus a 1× fact (5 + 1 = 6).
A 7× fact is calculated as a 5× fact plus a 2× fact (5 + 2 = 7).

A 4× fact is calculated as a 2× fact doubled (2 × 2 = 4).

This strategy also works with a subtraction. To take the 10× facts back to the 9× facts, a 9× fact is calculated as a 10× fact minus a 1× fact.

The 9× table is a good table for patterns. The patterns change this number which has an image of being difficult into a much friendlier number. As you may have guessed, these patterns appeal to me!

Let's look at the 9× table:

$1 \times 9 = 9$
$2 \times 9 = 18$
$3 \times 9 = 27$
$4 \times 9 = 36$ The answers have a pattern. If you add up
$5 \times 9 = 45$ the figures in any of the answers, the total is
$6 \times 9 = 54$ 9.
$7 \times 9 = 63 \ldots 6 + 3 = 9$
$8 \times 9 = 72$
$9 \times 9 = 81 \ldots 8 + 1 = 9$
$10 \times 9 = 90$

There is another pattern in the answers to the nine times table. If you look down the unit figures in the answer column you can see how they sequence down as 9, 8, 7, 6, 5, 4, 3, 2, 1, 0. The figures in the tens column also sequence, but in the opposite direction, upwards, starting with an unwritten zero (in $1 \times 9 = 09$) and ending at 9.

The answer to any number times 9 will have figures which ultimately add up to make 9. For example, $85\,461 \times 9 = 769\,149$. Now add all the figures in the answer, $7 + 6 + 9 + 1 + 4 + 9 = 36$. Add again, $3 + 6 = 9$.

Now, let's try another pattern in the 9× table. This pattern works beyond just the table facts to any number times 9. Once again, we take a harder number and relate it to an easy number. We will use the 10× facts to take us to 9× facts.

All this work is based on 9 being 1 less than 10, a relationship used on pp.33–36 for extending basic addition facts and again on p.58 for addition of shop prices.

You may find it helpful to use coins to illustrate the development of this idea. A 10p coin is 1p more than 9p. Change the order of this statement so that it reads that 9p is 1p less than 10p. If you took 2 ten pence coins, then 2 lots of 9p would be 2p less than these 2 ten pence coins. If you took 6 ten pence coins then 6 lots of 9p would be 6p less than the 6 ten pence coins.

Build up the 9× table in comparison with the 10× table:

1 nine is 1 less than 1 ten	$1 \times 9 = 1 \times 10 - 1$
2 nines are 2 less than 2 tens	$2 \times 9 = 2 \times 10 - 2$
3 nines are 3 less than 3 tens	$3 \times 9 = 3 \times 10 - 3$
4 nines are 4 less than 4 tens	$4 \times 9 = 4 \times 10 - 4$
5 nines are 5 less than 5 tens	$5 \times 9 = 5 \times 10 - 5$
6 nines are 6 less than 6 tens	$6 \times 9 = 6 \times 10 - 6$
7 nines are 7 less than 7 tens	$7 \times 9 = 7 \times 10 - 7$
8 nines are 8 less than 8 tens	$8 \times 9 = 8 \times 10 - 8$
9 nines are 9 less than 9 tens	$9 \times 9 = 9 \times 10 - 9$

The pattern is shown in this table. If you need to work out a 9× fact, start with a 10× fact. For example, 6 × 9 starts with 6 × 10 equals 60 and then subtracts 6 to make 54.

Again, if you want 8 × 9, start with 8 × 10 as 80 and subtract 8 to make 72. (You an check the answer by adding the figures. If they add to 9 you are correct and 7 + 2 does make 9.)

This technique works for any number times 9. Try 35 × 9 . . . 35 × 10 is 350. Now subtract 35 from 350 to obtain 315. Check by adding 3 + 1 + 5 which is 9.

This method for working out the nine times table facts is a classic example of using two easy steps to achieve one difficult step. Of course, if multiplying by nine is not a difficult step for you, you won't need to do this!

This two-step strategy can be used for multiplying (and dividing) by 4. To multiply by 4, you multiply by two, twice. For example, to answer 4 × 7:

Multiply 7 by 2 to give 14, then multiply by 2 again to get 28—that is:

$$7 \times 2 = 14 \quad \text{followed by} \quad 14 \times 2 = 28$$

To divide 784 by 4, use two steps:

$$784 \div 2 = 394 \quad \text{followed by} \quad 392 \div 2 = 196$$

The square numbers

All four sides of the square have the same length and all four angles are 90° (p.127).

The area of a square is calculated by the same method as that used to calculate the area of a rectangle—that is, to multiply length times width—except that these two lengths are the same in a square. So for a square with sides of length 5, the area is $5 \times 5 = 25$.

If a number is multiplied by itself as in 5×5, the answer is called a square number. The first ten square numbers are:

$$1 \times 1 = 1$$
$$2 \times 2 = 4$$
$$3 \times 3 = 9$$
$$4 \times 4 = 16$$
$$5 \times 5 = 25$$
$$6 \times 6 = 36$$
$$7 \times 7 = 49$$
$$8 \times 8 = 64$$
$$9 \times 9 = 81$$
$$10 \times 10 = 100$$

Mathematicians often use ways to write information as briefly as possible whilst retaining total clarity. The total clarity is only available if you know the code. The code for squares is:

$$5 \times 5 = 5^2$$
$$8 \times 8 = 8^2$$
$$10 \times 10 = 10^2$$

4 Add, Subtract, Multiply and Divide

Mathematicians call these the *four operations*. They are the four basic ways you manipulate (operate on) numbers and so it is very important that you spend a little time making sure you have a really good and clear understanding of what each operation means and also how they all relate to and link with each other.

Adding
Most people picture addition as sums such like these:

$$5 + 6 \qquad 29 + 37 \qquad \begin{array}{r} 436 \\ +278 \\ \hline \end{array}$$

but adding starts with counting. Counting 1, 2, 3, 4, 5 is adding 1 each time. Counting 2, 4, 6, 8 is adding 2 each time. Counting 10, 20, 30, 40, 50 is adding 10 each time.

Adding is putting together. For example, putting together 5 coins and 3 coins gives a total of 8 coins. Addition sums such as:

$$\begin{array}{r} 56 \\ +23 \\ \hline 79 \\ \hline \end{array}$$

involve putting together two numbers (56 and 23) to make a total of 79.

Subtracting

Subtracting usually conjures up images of sums such as:

$$9 - 3 \qquad 46 - 31 \qquad \begin{array}{r} 787 \\ -463 \\ \hline \end{array}$$

Subtraction is taking away, separating, and therefore it is the opposite of adding. This means that counting back 10, 9, 8, 7, 6 is also subtracting one each time. Counting back 8, 6, 4, 2 is subtracting two each time. Counting back 70, 60, 50, 40, 30 is subtracting ten each time.

The taking away and separating aspect of subtraction is illustrated in the following examples. If you have 8 coins and you take 3 away you have 5 left. You have separated the 8 coins into 3 coins and 5 coins.

Subtraction sums like:

$$\begin{array}{r} 98 \\ -46 \\ \hline 52 \\ \hline \end{array}$$

involve separating the number 98 into two parts. The number 46 is one part. By taking away 46 from 98 you find the second part, 52.

Multiplication

Multiplication is repeated addition, adding the same number several times. For example 7×6 is seven sixes added together—$6 + 6 + 6 + 6 + 6 + 6 + 6$. Although it would be possible, and mathematically correct, to work out 7×6 in this adding way, it is quicker to know the answer is 42 or work it out by a more efficient method than seven additions—for example, mixing adding and multiplying so that 7×6 is broken down into 5×6 plus 2×6 (see p.39).

It is very important to realise that multiplication is so closely related to adding. That it is really a special form of addition.

The method most people learned at school, called 'long multiplication', is really a mixture of addition and multiplication. I shall explain this in more detail on p.60.

Division

Division is dividing up into equal parts. It is the opposite of multiplication. This means it is also repeated subtraction, taking away the same number several times. For example, to divide 36 by 9, you could take away 9s successively until you reached zero:

$$36 - 9 = 27$$
$$27 - 9 = 18$$
$$18 - 9 = 9$$
$$9 - 9 = 0$$

Four 9s were taken away: $36 \div 9 = 4$

I hope you can see how the four operations—add, subtract, multiply and divide—are so closely related and how they can be mixed and blended to suit the way you want to work.

One of the big misconceptions about numeracy is that there is only one way to do something. It is possible to use ideas such as the link between addition and multiplication to provide alternative methods of calculation.

THE TRADITIONAL METHODS FOR ADDITION AND SUBTRACTION

These are the written methods which involve 'carrying' and 'borrowing' and 'decomposing'. These words are a good illustration of the point I made on p.14 about the language of maths. They all have other meanings which have nothing to do with maths. This handicaps their usefulness in that it is less likely learners will attach an image, a picture or visual meaning to these words that will link them to maths.

Nevertheless, I shall now embark on explanations that will use these words (and some alternatives which, in my biased opinion, are better). I shall work through in detail the addition of two numbers to get a total and then do the same for a subtraction using the same numbers and taking the total apart again. This should illustrate again that addition and subtraction are the same processes in reverse. It might even make the 'carrying' and 'decomposing' clearer.

So, even if you think you are an expert at addition, humour me and work through the explanation.

The *addition* example is:

$$187$$
$$-269$$

To help you develop a clear picture of the steps, try using 1p coins (for units), 10p coins (for tens) and £1 coins (for hundreds).

Set up the coins.

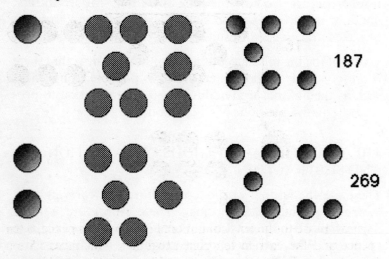

In the written method you start at the units. Since addition is putting together, move the 7 one pence coins and 9 one pence coins together. This gives 16 coins. Exchange (trade) ten 1p coins for one 10p coin.

Trading or exchanging ten units for one ten, one ten for ten units, ten tens for one hundred, one hundred for ten tens and so on is a fundamental manoeuvre in numeracy. I always think of it in terms of reducing the number of coins I have in my pocket.

16 is a two-figure number, 1 (ten) and 6 (units). The 6 stays in the units column and the ten is (naturally) moved to the tens column. This is the 'carry' number.

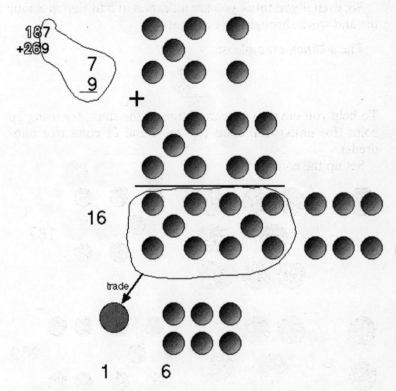

Now move to the tens column and put the 8 ten pence, 6 ten pence and the carried ten pence together. This gives 15 ten pence coins. Exchange (trade) ten 10p coins for one £1 coin, which makes £1 and 50p (5 ten pence coins). The 5 ten pence coins stay in the tens column and the pound (hundred) is moved (carried) to the hundreds column.

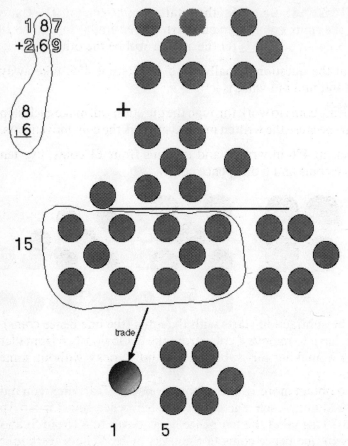

All that remains is to put together the hundreds, the £1 coins. Add together the 1 and the 2 from the sum and add in the carried 1 to make 4 hundreds. The addition is complete:

$$\begin{array}{r} 187 \\ +269 \\ \hline 456 \end{array}$$

The coins follow exactly the same process as the written method. This makes them useful image reinforcers.

The *subtraction* example uses the same numbers and separates the total into its two parts again.

```
456   the total
-187   one part
_____   the answer will be the other part
```

What the question actually 'says' is: 'Here is 456, take away 187 and find out what is left.'

Using coins to work through the question will make each step clear, because the written method mirrors the coin movements.

Set up 456 in writing and in coins (four £1 coins, five ten pence coins and 6 one pence coins):

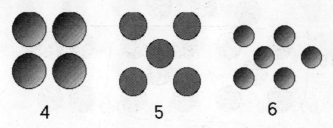

The subtraction starts with the units (the one pence coins). You have to remove 7 coins from the 6. Obviously 6 is smaller than 7, making this subtraction a little tricky without some adjustment.

To obtain more 1p coins, you reverse the 'carrying' you did for addition. Exchange or trade a ten pence coin for ten 1p coins. This takes the ten pence coins down to 4 (from 5) and puts 16 one pence coins in the units place. School textbooks call this 'decomposition' because you have decomposed the 456 into four hundreds, four tens and sixteen units.

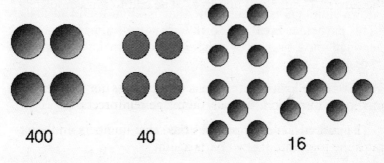

Now take away 7 one pence coins, leaving 9 one pence coins. (This is the units figure of your answer.) Move on to the tens . . .

There are now 4 tens and you need to take away 8. As 4 is less than 8, again you have to trade (decompose the number). Again do the opposite trade you did in the addition. Trade one of the £1 (hundred) coins for ten 10p coins. This leaves 3 hundreds (three £1 coins). Put the 10p coins in the tens column to make 14 ten pence coins altogether.

3 x 100 = 300   14 x 10 = 140

Now you can take away 8 tens, leaving 6 as the tens figure of your answer.

The last step is to subtract in the hundreds column. There are 3 hundreds (three £1 coins) left. Take away 1 to leave 2 hundreds as your answer in the hundreds place value column.

Looking back, the complete answer is 269, which, of course is the number you added to 187 to make 456.

This decomposition method breaks down a number into parts which are more suitable for the subtraction. Breaking down numbers is a technique that is often useful in maths. This particular breaking down technique is aimed to produce enough units, or tens, or hundreds, etc., to make a subtraction possible.

In 456 the units and the tens figures were not large enough for the subtraction. 456 was decomposed or renamed as:

3 hundreds, 14 tens and 16 units

This is still 456 . . .   300   3 hundreds
                     400   14 tens
                    + 16   16 units
                     456

This is another example of maths using the breaking down and building up numbers strategy in order to make a calculation easier.

Here are two ways to write down this method of subtraction:

the messy $\overset{3\ 14}{4}\overset{1}{5}6$ the middle line   4 5 6

               -187 3 14 16

                269                          $-1\ 8\ 7$

                                          2 6 9

DOING SUBTRACTION 'IN YOUR HEAD'

The written method described above would ask a great deal of your short-term memory, the memory you will use while working out this subtraction, holding the figures in your mind while you move through each step. There is another disadvantage in the method above. In this written method you work from units to hundreds, so you move across to the left, having to hold the unit and tens figures in your brain, with no practice or repetition as you move on to new figures, which may well confuse your memory's hold on the earlier figures. The final answer presents these digits in the reverse order to the way in which you did the calculation.

If you work in the direction from hundreds to units, you can repeat the numbers in the evolving answer as you work along—the *'hundreds to units'* method (the explanation takes a lot longer than the method!):

$$456 - 187$$

Start at the hundreds: 4 (hundred) minus 1 (hundred) = 3 (hundred).

Move to ten: 5 (tens) minus 8 (tens) . . . needs some help, so take 10 tens (1 hundred) from the 3 hundred, leaving 2 hundred and making the 5 tens up to 15 tens, then:

15 (tens) minus 8 (tens) = 7 (tens)

Alternatively you could take 80 from 350.
The answer, so far, is two hundred and seventy.

Move to units: 6 (units) minus 7 (units) . . . needs some help so take 10 units (1 ten) from the two hundred and seventy, leaving two hundred and sixty and making the 6 units up to 16, then:

16 (units) minus 7 (units) = 9 (units)

Alternatively you could take 7 from 276.
The answer is 269.

Now try the *adding on method*, which again uses the fact that addition and subtraction are reversals of the same idea.

456 – 187

Start at 187 and add on numbers until you reach the target number of 456. Use sensible stages (go for tens, hundreds, thousands and so on).

187 plus 3 is 190
190 plus 10 is 200 . . . so far 13 added on
200 plus 200 is 400 . . . so far 213 added on
400 plus 56 is 456 . . . 213 + 56 is 269 added on.

You could add the 56 in two stages, first 50, then 6.
This method uses a running total. The repetition of the numbers at each stage helps the short-term memory retain the numbers.

Two ways to add a column of numbers
This is a difficult task for many people. If they use a calculator, they often make a mistake at one stage and get the total wrong. The two methods described below are quite different from each other, but both provide real support for the adding process.

1   The tally method

(The description is longer than the method. This particular method tends to appeal to inchworms rather than grasshoppers).

$$
\begin{array}{r}
^{4}46 \\
\cancel{78} \\
6\cancel{5} \\
9\cancel{3} \\
2\cancel{8} \\
57 \\
\cancel{44} \\
+38 \\
\hline
449
\end{array}
$$

Start at the top of the units column and add 6 + 8 = 14. Draw a slash through the 8 (this tally represents the ten from 14) and carry on adding down with the 4 (from the 14) added to the 5 to make 9. Next number 3 + 9 = 12. Draw a slash through the 3 (this tally represents the ten from the 12) and carry on adding down, 2 + 8 = 10. Draw a slash through the 8 to represent another ten. Add on down 7 + 4 = 11. Another slash, through the 4. Add on down 1 + 8 = 9. The 9 goes in the units column as its total.

Now count the tally marks (slashes). There are four, 4, tallies. This represents 4 tens to write at the top of the tens column.

Now add down the tens column using the same tally method, but each tally mark is now worth one hundred, 100.
4 + 4 = 8. Then 8 + 7 = 15, so a slash through the 7 represents a hundred and the 5 is carried on. 5 + 6 = 11. A slash through the 6 represents another 100.

Carry on adding down the column. 1 + 9 = 10. Another slash for another 100, through the 9. Adding down again, 2 + 5 = 7. Then 7 + 4 = 11. Draw a slash for another 100 through the 4.
1 + 3 = 4. Write as the total of the tens column.

Count the slashes or tallies for the 100s. There are four, 4.
Write 4 as the total in the hundreds column.

This makes the final answer 449.

2   *The casting out tens method*

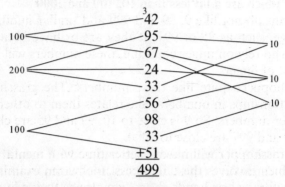

In this method you look within each column for pairs or
triplets of numbers which add up to 10 or 20.
    From the units column:

    2 + 5 + 3 = 10 . . . cross out 2, 5 and 3
    7 + 3 = 10 . . . cross out 7 and 3   There are 3 tens.
    4 + 6 = 10 . . . cross out 4 and 6

All that is left is 8 + 1 = 9.
    9 is the total for the units column.

The 3 from the 3 tens is written at the top of the tens
column.

From the tens column:

    4 + 6 = 10 . . . cross out 4 and 6   There are 4 tens
    9 + 2 + 9 = 20 . . . cross out 9, 2 and 9   from the tens
    5 + 5 = 10 . . . cross out 5 and 5   column (which
                                                 are actually 100s).

All that is left is 3 + 3 + 3 = 9.

    9 is the total for the tens column.

The 4 from the 4 hundreds is written in the hundreds column.

The answer is 499.

Nine, ninety-nine, nine hundred and ninety-nine and other numbers which are a bit less than 10, 100 and 1000

Inchworms do not like 9, 99 and 999 and similar numbers in this range, such as 95 or 997. If they are or have been inchworms who rely on finger counting, these numbers will represent a lot of fingers.

Grasshoppers quite like these numbers. The grasshopper sees relationships in numbers. She relates them to other, usually easier numbers. So 9 is close to 10, 99 and 95 are close to 100, 999 and 997 are close to 1000.

The grasshopper will have a better time with mental arithmetic which involves these numbers. Inchworm examination setters will rub their hands in sadistic glee as they pile on the 9s in the questions they see as difficult (for other inchworms).

For mental arithmetic questions involving these numbers, it is worth learning some grasshopper techniques. Inchworms will by their nature try to use their written methods to do mental arithmetic and many of these methods will make too much demand on their (short-term) memory for them to succeed. It is hard for an inchworm to adopt grasshopper methods (and vice versa), but it is worth them persevering (and overcoming the feeling that if it is easier they must be cheating).

To illustrate this, let's return to an example similar to that on p.16. I will explain how an inchworm and a grasshopper solve a mental subtraction, 422 – 98. As I explain each method, think about the demands of the method on aspects of memory.

The inchworm would rather do this sum on paper. Since this is not allowed in mental maths, he will try to replicate the method in his head. He has to visualise the question as he would write it:

$$422$$
$$-98$$

The next step depends on whether he uses renaming (decomposition) or the equal additions method. Let's say he uses renaming:

$$\begin{array}{r} {\scriptstyle 1\ 1} \\ 4\cancel{2}2 \\ -98 \\ \hline \end{array}$$

He also has to rename (decompose) the 4:

$$\begin{array}{r} {\scriptstyle 3\ 1\ 1} \\ \cancel{4}\cancel{2}2 \\ -98 \\ \hline \end{array}$$

Now, holding all this in his memory, he subtracts to obtain 324.

The grasshopper sees the 98 as 2 less than 100, subtracts 100 to get 322 and adds back 2, since subtracting 100 gave a smaller answer than subtracting 98. Answer: 324.

The same principles can be used when shopping. For example, books tend to be priced as £6.99, £14.99, or some amount of pounds and 99p. Inchworms will simply try to add the prices as written, which is quite difficult in that such an addition has many steps. Grasshoppers will round up each price, for example, £6.99 to £7 and £14.99 to £15, add them to get £22 and then, if they consider the detail worth it, readjust to an accurate answer (£21.98).

For example, a grasshopper will add: £4.99 + £19.99 + £6.99 as £5 + £20 + £7 to a total of £32. The readjustment is by subtracting $3 \times 1p = 13p$ from £32 to give £31.97.

This example shows how the numbers have been simplified to give a reduced number of figures so that, if trying to work this out mentally, the load on memory is greatly reduced.

Another grasshopper skill is the clustering or pairing of less easy numbers into easy numbers, for example ten (see p.56 for another use of this strategy).

The following example appears in a GCSE maths textbook: 'Add together mentally, 9, 2, 3 and 6.' The book then goes on to add them one at a time in the order given.

If you look at these numbers, that is *take time to overview*, the 3 and 6 make 9, the 2 can be split into 1 and 1, making the two 9s into two tens and the answer into 20.

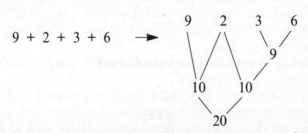

Multiplying by 10, 100, 1000, 10 000 and more
This is a useful and easy process. It is easy because it follows a simple pattern. First I shall show you the pattern. Then I'll explain the maths behind the pattern.

$43 \times 10 = 430$
$43 \times 100 = 4300$
$43 \times 1000 = 43\ 000$
$43 \times 10\ 000 = 430\ 000$
$43 \times 100\ 000 = 4\ 300\ 000$

The pattern is in the zeros. The numbers of zeros on each side of the equals signs are the same.

The pattern is, like any good pattern, predictable. When you multiply by 100, with its two zeros, these two zeros appear in the answer, pushing place values up by 100 times—that is, two place values. When you multiply by 1000, with its three zeros, these three zeros appear in the answer, pushing place values up by 1000 times.

The maths is simple (trust me).

If a number is multiplied by 10 it gets 10 times bigger. If a number is multiplied by 100 it gets 100 times bigger. If a number is multiplied by 1000 it gets 1000 times bigger. And so on.

How do we know a number is 10 times bigger, or 100 times bigger, or 1000 times bigger, or so on?

There are two points to look for. The first is that the figures
in the number are the same, but have some zeros tacked on the
end. The second is that the place values of the figures in the
number have increased. For example, if you select the 4 from
the 43. In 43, the 4 represents 40. The 4 has a tens place value.

In $43 \times 10 = 430$, the 4 moves from a tens place value to a
hundreds place value.

In $43 \times 100 = 4300$, the 4 has moved from a tens place value
to a thousands place value.

In $43 \times 1000 = 43\ 000$, the 4 has moved from a tens place
value to a ten thousands place value.

After the section on decimal numbers we can look at dividing by 10, 100, 1000, 10 000 and so on.

Long multiplication, or a confusing mixture of addition and multiplication

Somewhere, sometime, someone probably explained long
multiplication to you. You were probably too young at the
time to appreciate the structure of the procedure. To use the
analogy of UK film ratings, I always felt it had a 12 certificate,
but was forced onto a PG audience.

Short multiplication is one step, for example $10 \times 5 = 50$ is
definitely one step. $16 \times 2 = 32$ is one step for most, but . . .

Long multiplication is definitely more than one step, but it
is just another version of the strategy I described for working
out 6×4 (p.39). For 6×4, the multiplication was related to
repeated addition, addition of 4 six times.

$$
\begin{array}{r}
4 \\
4 \\
4 \\
4 \\
4 \\
+4 \\
\hline
\end{array}
$$

To avoid a step-by-step addition of $4 + 4 + 4 + 4 + 4 + 4$,
the sum can be grouped as 5×4 plus 1×4, which is a mixture
of addition and multiplication.

The technique can be extended to other multiplications, for example:

12 × 7, which is 7 + 7 + 7 + 7 + 7 + 7 + 7 + 7 + 7 + 7 + 7 + 7

The twelve 7s can be clustered into two groups, one of ten 7s and one of two 7s

$$12 \times 7 \quad \text{is} \quad 10 \times 7 \quad \text{plus} \quad 2 \times 7$$

The multiplication has been broken down into two easier parts, 10 × 7 (= 70) and 2 × 7 (= 14). The two parts are added (70 + 14) to give the answer as 84.

This procedure extends into 'long multiplication'. In this procedure the multiplication is broken down into manageable parts. The traditional breakdown is automatic. It is usual to split the numbers according to their place values. For example, to multiply 48 by 35, the split is to 30 and 5, so you multiply 48 by 30 and 48 by 5 and then add the two parts together. To multiply 521 by 426, the split is to do one multiplication of 521 by 400, then 521 by 20 and a third multiplication of 521 by 6. These three multiplication sub-answers are then added to show the answer to a multiplication 521 by 426.

For example: 48 × 35

$$48 \times 30 = 1440 \qquad 48 \times 5 = 240$$
$$1440 + 240 = 1680$$

This is traditionally set out as shown below:

```
      48
     ×35
    1440      this is 48 × 30
     240      this is 48 × 5
    1680      this is 48 × 35
```

I have found that a visual image can sometimes help with understanding this multiplication. A sum like 48 × 35 is the same as a calculation to work out the area of a rectangle with sides of 48 and 35.

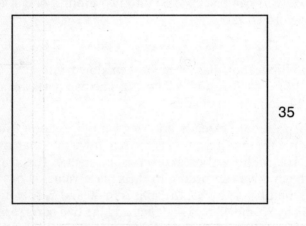

If the rectangle is broken down into two sub-areas, using the place value split into units and tens for 35, you have a picture of the two parts of the multiplication.

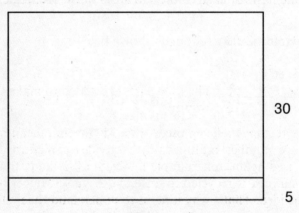

It is, of course, also possible to split a rectangle into four sub-areas, for example 42 × 53:

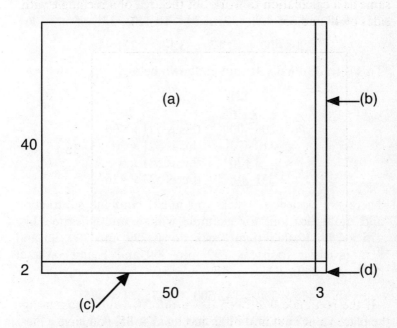

The multiplication of the numbers 42 × 53 can be done in four parts, one part for each of the sub areas of the rectangle:

42 × 53
a) 40 × 50 = 2000
b) 40 × 3 = 120
c)   2 × 50 = 100
d)   2 × 3 =   6   The four parts are added to make the
42 × 53 = 2226   answer.

Using a rectangle to represent a two-figure number times a two-figure number multiplication provides a picture which can be used again, for example in algebra. So many times in maths, an idea is recycled in different disguises, but it is still the same idea. That's why it helps to understand the first time you meet an idea, but also it illustrates how each new interpretation of an idea can make that idea stronger in your mind.

Now, a longer example of long multiplication: 521×426

426 is $400 + 20 + 6$

$521 \times 400 = 208\ 400 \quad 521 \times 20 = 10\ 420 \quad 521 \times 6 = 3\ 126$

$208\ 400 + 10\ 420 + 3\ 126 = 221\ 946$

This is traditionally set out as shown below:

```
      521
     ×426
  208 400      this is 521 × 400
   10 420      this is 521 × 20
    3 126      this is 521 × 6
  221 946      this is 521 × 426
```

There are occasions when you might combine subtraction and multiplication, for example with a multiplication like 475×299. Rather than break down 299 into 200, 90 and 9, it is easier to break 299 into 300 and 1 and subtract $(300 - 1 = 299)$.

$$475 \times 300 = 142\ 500 \qquad 475 \times 1 = 475$$

$$475 \times 299 = 142\ 500 - 475 = 142\ 025$$

INDICES

Indices are another bit of maths code. Look at these two examples:

the area of a square which has sides of length 5 is $\quad 5 \times 5$

5×5 is also written as $\quad 5^2 \qquad$ (see also p.43)

This is also named as 'five squared' or 'five to the *power* of 2'.

the volume of a cube which has sides of length 5 is $5 \times 5 \times 5$

$5 \times 5 \times 5$ is also written as $\quad 5^3$

This is also called 'five cubed' or 'five to the *power* of 3'.

It would be logical to follow this pattern and write

$5 \times 5 \times 5 \times 5$ is also written as 5^4

This is also expressed as 'five to the *power* of four'.

Indices are useful with powers of ten. This time the logic of the sequential pattern can be taken forwards and backwards. First the forward pattern:

$10 \times 10 = 10^2 = 100$
$10 \times 10 \times 10 = 10^3 = 1000$
$10 \times 10 \times 10 \times 10 = 10^4 = 10\ 000$
$10 \times 10 \times 10 \times 10 \times 10 = 10^5 = 100\ 000$
$10 \times 10 \times 10 \times 10 \times 10 \times 10 = 10^6 = 1\ 000\ 000$

Now the backwards pattern:

$1000 = 10 \times 10 \times 10 = 10^3$
$100 = 10 \times 10 = 10^2$
$10 = 10 = 10^1$
$1 = 10^0$
$0.1 = \dfrac{1}{10} = 10^{-1}$
$0.01 = \dfrac{1}{100} = \dfrac{1}{10 \times 10} = 10^{-2}$
$0.001 = \dfrac{1}{1000} = \dfrac{1}{10 \times 10 \times 10} = 10^{-3}$

DIVISION THE EASIER WAY

The procedure called long division (such as $24\overline{)12744}$) is generally considered to be difficult. If long multiplication has a 12 certificate, long division, in its traditional format, has a 15, verging on 18, certificate. It certainly requires you to use a lot of maths sub-skills. Of course, you can use a calculator, but if you do you should always be able to do at least a rough mental check to give an estimate.

Division on a calculator often results in people using the

keys in the wrong order. For example, 24)$\overline{12744}$ is keyed in correctly as (1) 12744

          (2) ÷

          (3) 24

          (4) =

which is a change in the order in which the sum was presented.

There is an alternative method (which also happens to have a built-in estimate). I give this a PG, maybe 12 certificate.

The method is based on multiplication and division being the same, but opposite. A basic example should explain this . . .

Seven times nine equals sixty-three $7 \times 9 = 63$

This fact also tells us that there are seven nines in sixty-three, which is one of the ways of saying that sixty-three divided by nine is seven.

$$63 \div 9 = 7$$

(It also tells us that sixty-three divided by seven is nine: $63 \div 7 = 9$. Every multiplication fact is two division facts.)

So if 63 is to be divided by 9, you could look at this sum as a multiplication with one number missing (the answer):

$$63 = 9 \times ?$$

This missing multiplier is the basis of the method for division. For example:

$$24)\overline{12744}$$

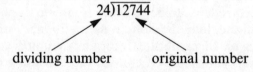

dividing number   original number

In this method you are finding out what number multiplies the dividing number to give the original number, so the example becomes:

$$12744 = 24 \times ?$$

The division has been turned into a multiplication, another

example of the usefulness of rewording maths questions. This is the first stage of this alternative method for division. The next stage is to set up a simple table. This gives easy multiples of 24. Look for the pattern in the numbers in the table. See how the figures 24, 48 and 12 keep recurring? The number of zeros shows when you have multiplied by 10, 100 or 1000 times 24 (see p.59):

1 × 24	24
2 × 24	48
3 × 24	120
10 × 24	240
20 × 24	480
50 × 24	1200
100 × 24	2400
200 × 24	4800
500 × 24	12000

Work on building the table can stop at this point, because 12 000 is close to the number we are dividing. We have now worked out an estimate.

It should be obvious that the answer is going to be a little bigger than 500, since 500 × 24 is 12 000, which is close to 12 744.

To get the accurate answer, all you have to do is a few subtractions, using the multiplication facts from the table and keeping count of how many 24s you have taken away. Keep the layout organised . . .

12744		
−12000	500	× 24
744		
−480	20	× 24
264		
−240	10	× 24
24		
−24	1	× 24
0	531	× 24

The answer is 531: 531 × 24 = 12 744.

Try another example . . . 3960 ÷ 24 . . .? × 24 = 3960.

A look down the 24× table shows the answer is between 100 and 200, closer to 200:

3960		
−2400	100	× 24
1560		
−1200	50	× 24
360		
−240	10	× 24
120		
−120	5	× 24
0	165	× 24

The answer is ? × 24 = 3960 is 165.

5   Fractions

If I wanted to create maths anxiety I would pick on fractions. For many people they seem to be the final straw in their attempts to understand maths.

I think the reason is that fractions seem to have their own rules. Whatever logic learners have struggled to achieve so far seems to be destroyed by these rather different numbers.

Once again I shall work from the principle that you know more than you realise. Fractions, or at least some fractions, are all around us and are part of our everyday life. You can use your familiarity with these to develop an understanding of other fractions.

GETTING THE PICTURE

Where do you meet fractions? Which ones do you meet? Here are a few common examples:

SALES

SALE
1/2
price

$\frac{1}{2}$ **price**

TIME

¼ past 7

AGE

HAPPY 8 ¾ BIRTHDAY

8 and ¾

Most people in Britain know what a *half* and a *quarter* mean as we meet these fractions more than any others, especially since the UK 'went metric' and eliminated a lot of other fractions based on 'old' units like 16 ounces and 36 inches. If you can understand half and quarter then you can take this understanding to other fractions, because, like all mathematics, rules are rules and all fractions will behave the same way.

Let's look at half and quarter, written as $\frac{1}{2}$ and $\frac{1}{4}$ respectively.

Firstly $\frac{1}{2}$ uses two numbers (1 and 2) with the 1 written on top of the 2 and a line to separate them. The same is true of $\frac{1}{4}$ or $\frac{3}{4}$ or any other fraction such as $\frac{1}{10}$.

Fractions use two numbers, one on top of the other and separated by a line. So, for example:

$\frac{5}{6}$ is a fraction called five sixths.
$\frac{7}{11}$ is a fraction called seven elevenths (not to be confused with a chain of convenience stores).

Now, because a half and a quarter are well known they have developed names which are not in the normal pattern of fraction names. If $\frac{1}{2}$ were to follow the pattern it should be one second and $\frac{1}{4}$ should be one fourth (as it sometimes is in the USA). So you must direct your attention to the numbers in these two fractions and they will lead you to an understanding of all fractions.

HOW A FRACTION IS 'MADE'

I want you to start by using something you can handle to illustrate the maths. This time use a piece of paper, say a sheet of A4 or a page cut neatly out of one of those weekend newspaper magazines.

Take this sheet of paper. This will be your one whole (one sheet) . . . 1.

Now fold it exactly in two. This creates two halves (which

must be exactly the same size). There are now two, 2, parts
together. One, 1, of these parts is one half, one out of two
parts, $\frac{1}{2}$.

In the fraction $\frac{1}{2}$:

this line means divided➤ **1**◄the number of parts you have

            2◄the number of parts the
                whole has been divided into

So, the whole, 1, has been divided into 2 parts and you have 1
of these parts . . . a half, $\frac{1}{2}$.

Now fold the paper in half again, which creates four quarters. Each one of these parts is one quarter, one out of four
parts, $\frac{1}{4}$.

In the fraction $\frac{1}{4}$:

this line means divided➤ **1**◄the number of parts you have

            4◄the number of parts the
                whole has been divided into

So, the whole has been divided into four parts and you have
one of them . . . a quarter, $\frac{1}{4}$.

This will work with any fraction, for example $\frac{3}{4}$:

$$\frac{3}{4}$$

The 4 and the line mean the whole has been divided into 4
parts. The 3 means that you have 3 of these 4 parts . . . three
fourths or three quarters.

Make $\frac{3}{4}$ with a sheet of paper. Fold it in half one way and
then fold this folded paper in half again the other way. This
gives 4 equal parts. Cut off one quarter to leave $\frac{3}{4}$.

Use $\frac{3}{4}$ with time . . . $\frac{3}{4}$ of an hour . . .
One hour is 60 minutes.

One quarter, $\frac{1}{4}$ of an hour, is 60 minutes divided by 4, that
is 15 minutes.

Three quarters, $\frac{3}{4}$ of an hour, is 3 × one quarter, that is 3 × 15, that is 45 minutes.

Use $\frac{3}{4}$ with age . . . $\frac{3}{4}$ of a year . . .
One year is 12 months.

One quarter, $\frac{1}{4}$ of a year, is 12 months divided by 4, that is 3 months. Three quarters, $\frac{3}{4}$ of a year, is 3 × 3 months, that is 9 months.

Other versions of a half . . . and other fractions
The simplest way of writing a half in numbers is $\frac{1}{2}$. This means you have 1 out of 2 parts . . . a half.

But what about half a year, half of 12 months? This is $\frac{6}{12}$ . . . you have 6 out of 12 months.

What about half of £1? This is 50 pence out of 100 pence. This is $\frac{50}{100}$ . . . you have 50 out of 100 pence.

What about half an hour, half of 60 minutes? This is $\frac{30}{60}$ . . . you have 30 out of 60 minutes.

So far we have four ways of writing a half as fraction numbers:

$$\frac{1}{2} \qquad \frac{6}{12} \qquad \frac{50}{100} \qquad \frac{30}{60}$$

Can you see what connects these four ways together? Can you see the pattern?

In each of these versions of a half, the top number is half the value of the bottom number.

Write some more versions of a half, for example half of a kilogram which is half of 1000 grams.

Any fraction, then is made up from two numbers, separated by a line:

$$\frac{a}{b} \qquad \frac{5}{7}$$

$\frac{a}{b}$ represents ANY fraction. $\frac{5}{7}$ is a particular example.

Always consider the bottom number first. It tells you how

many parts in the fraction and therefore the name of the fraction. So in $\frac{5}{7}$ the bottom number is 7, there are a total of seven parts and the fraction's name is sevenths. In the general fraction $\frac{a}{b}$, the bottom number is 'b', there are a total of b parts and the fraction's name is 'b'ths ('beeths').

This bottom number tells us how many parts the one (whole) has been divided into and the top number tells you how many of these parts you have. So $\frac{1}{2}$ is one out of two parts and $\frac{1}{3}$ is one out of three parts and $\frac{1}{4}$ is one out of four parts. The bigger the bottom number, the more parts the one (whole) has been divided into. This can confuse those unwise in the ways of fractions who might connect big numbers with big values. Remember the bottom number tells you how many times the one has been divided up, so $\frac{1}{1000}$, one thousandth, will be a much smaller quantity than $\frac{1}{5}$, one fifth. Those two letters, 'th', at the end of the number make a big difference to the meaning of the number.

For example, the th *effect makes one thousand*th *a number which is one million times smaller than one thousand.*

Now look at the top number. It tells you how many of the fraction parts you have. So in $\frac{5}{7}$, the top number is 5 which means you have 5 out of 7 parts. In the general fraction $\frac{a}{b}$, the top number is 'a' which means you have 'a' out of 'b' parts.

In the vocabulary of maths, 'out of' means divide.

Some more examples

'13'
60

The bottom number is 60 so the fraction is sixtieths. The whole has been divided into 60 parts. The top number is 13 which means the fraction is 13 out of 60 parts.

'52'
52

The bottom number is 52, which means the whole has been divided into 52 parts. The top number is also 52, which means the fraction is 52 out of 52 parts. Since this is ALL of the parts, this particular fraction must also be (a whole) one.

Any fraction which has the same number for the top number AND the bottom number is one (such as $\frac{4}{4}$, $\frac{7}{7}$, $\frac{60}{60}$, $\frac{365}{365}$).

'$\frac{3}{2}$'

The bottom number is 2, which means the whole has been divided into two parts, the fraction is named half. The top number is 3, so the fraction is 3 halves. Since the top number has a bigger value than the bottom number, the fraction must be worth more than one. In this example the fraction can also be written as $1\frac{1}{2}$, one and one half.

MULTIPLYING AND DIVIDING WITH FRACTIONS

This is a danger zone. But only if you don't know the rules. At the start of this chapter I said that fractions seem to have their own rules. This is even more true when multiplying and dividing with them.

Some people rashly (and wrongly) associate multiplying with making answers that are bigger and think that dividing always makes answers smaller. This is not true when using fractions which have a value of less than one.

Let's work from the familiar, in this case a half, to the general and once more build on what you know.

Fractions times whole numbers

Examine the question, 'What is half of £10?' The word 'of' means multiply, so the question needs you to multiply £10 by a half, yet the answer is £5 which is smaller than £10. So multiplying can make numbers smaller.

The explanation is quite straightforward. Again you need to use the maths code. The question can be written as

$$\tfrac{1}{2} \times 10 \div 5$$

What is hidden in this question is the divide sign in the fraction. $\frac{1}{2}$ can also be written as $1 \div 2$, so the question hides an extra maths operation and is

$$1 \times 10 \div 2$$

In a question like 'What is $\frac{2}{5}$ of £40?' a knowledge of the maths code is needed again. The question first becomes

$$\frac{2}{5} \times 40$$

The upper numbers are multiplied to become

$$\frac{80}{5}$$

The divide sign hidden in the fraction can then be used:

$$£80 \div 5 = £16$$

Fraction times fraction
For example: $\frac{2}{5} \times \frac{3}{4} = \frac{6}{20} = \frac{3}{10}$

There are two observations about this:

1   The answer is smaller than either of the multiplying fractions. It does not fall in between . . . ever.
2   The multiplication sign acts twice:
    once to multiply the two top numbers (2×3);
    second to multiply the two bottom numbers (5×4).

Dividing by fractions
I have just explained how multiplying by fractions can make an answer smaller. It should not, therefore, be too much of a shock to learn that dividing by fractions can make an answer bigger.

Dividing by a fraction whose value is less than one makes the answer bigger.

Let's start with two examples which should be familiar:

1   There are two quarter-hours in each half-hour. Written as numbers, this statement looks like this:

$$\tfrac{1}{2} \div \tfrac{1}{4} = 2$$

2   There are two half-hours in every hour. Written as numbers this statement looks like this:

$$1 \div \tfrac{1}{2} = 2$$

Quite often people give the answer 5 to the question, 'What is 10 divided by a half?' The answer is 20.

I tend to find it more interesting to try to understand how people get a wrong answer than to understand how they get a correct answer. One reason for this is that there are usually more ways to get things wrong and the wrong ways belong to the individual. The right ways have generally been learnt from someone else.

In the question above the most likely reason for producing the incorrect answer 5 is that people focus on the words 'half' and 'divide' separately rather than together in the phrase 'divided by a half'. 'Divide' is usually interpreted as making smaller and 'half' is usually interpreted as making smaller, so both suggest an answer of 5.

However, this deceptively simple question hides the mathematical equivalent of two wrongs make a right, interpreted here as two divides make a multiply.

The first divide is obvious: 'What is 10 *divided* by a half?' The second divide is hidden in the word 'half', just as for multiplication by fractions. A half is $\frac{1}{2}$ which translates to $1 \div 2$.

A way to deal with questions which include dividing by a fraction, such as 'What is 20 divided by a quarter?', is to take the number in its fraction form, $\frac{1}{4}$, and invert the numbers to $\frac{4}{1}$ and then multiply (instead of divide). So:

$$20 \div \tfrac{1}{4} \qquad \text{becomes} \qquad 20 \times \tfrac{4}{1} = 80$$

Another example, $60 \div \frac{3}{5}$:

$$60 \div \tfrac{3}{5} \qquad \text{becomes} \qquad 60 \times \tfrac{5}{3} = \tfrac{300}{3} = 100$$

When faced with a multiplication or division by fractions, a valuable strategy is to ask yourself the question, 'Will the answer be bigger, smaller or the same?'

For example, $15 \times \frac{1}{3}$ gives a smaller answer.
$40 \div \frac{1}{5}$ gives a bigger answer.

Another helpful strategy is to reword the question until it makes sense. For example, 'What is 40 divided by one fifth?'

is quite an abstract question, whereas 'how many fifths are there in 40?' should suggest a bigger answer.

To summarise:

MULTIPLYING
by 1 gives an answer which is the same value;
by numbers bigger than 1 gives bigger answers;
by numbers less than 1 gives smaller answers.

DIVIDING
by 1 gives an answer which is the same value;
by numbers bigger than 1 gives smaller answers;
by numbers smaller than 1 gives bigger answers.

ADDING AND SUBTRACTING WITH FRACTIONS

Once again, let's work from what you know.

You have already taken away $\frac{1}{4}$ from $\frac{4}{4}$ (one whole) to obtain $\frac{3}{4}$. You probably know that two halves make 1 whole ($\frac{1}{2}$ plus $\frac{1}{2}$ = $\frac{2}{2}$ = 1) and also that $\frac{1}{2}$ plus $\frac{1}{4}$ is $\frac{3}{4}$.

This takes you a good way towards understanding how to add and subtract fractions.

Golden Rule 1
Only do addition or subtraction for fractions when they have, or have been changed to have, the same number on the bottom (which means you may have to adjust one or more fractions).

For example: $\frac{1}{5} + \frac{3}{5}$ is OK to add straight away;

but $\frac{1}{5} + \frac{2}{3}$ needs some adjustment to the bottom numbers before the fractions can be added (to be explained later).

Golden Rule 2
When the fractions have the same bottom number, only add or subtract the top numbers.

For example: $\frac{1}{2} + \frac{1}{2} = \frac{2}{2}$

and $\frac{3}{5} - \frac{1}{5} = \frac{2}{5}$

Explaining the Golden Rules

Start from what you know:

$$\tfrac{1}{2} + \tfrac{1}{2} = \tfrac{2}{2}$$

In this addition, the bottom number stays as 2, but the top numbers are added. If you say the fraction sum in words the addition starts to make sense:

'One half plus one half equals two halves'. The bottom number is used as the name of the fraction—it identifies it, in this example as a half. It is only possible to add directly fractions which have the same name (the same number on the bottom).

To deal with fractions which have different names—that is different numbers as their bottom line—start with an example which is familiar:

$$\tfrac{1}{2} + \tfrac{1}{4} = \tfrac{3}{4}$$

In this example, the numbers on the bottom of the two fractions which are to be added are different. One fraction is a half and the other is a quarter. They have different names so they cannot be added directly.

The half has to be adjusted, or renamed.

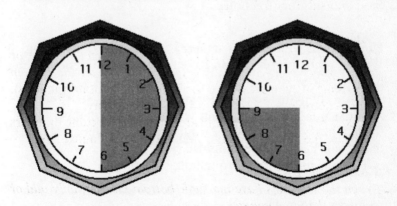

Most people know about half and quarter hours on a clock.

Two quarters make a half. In numbers this is:

$$\tfrac{2}{4} = \tfrac{1}{2}$$

Remember, a half can take many forms, so long as the top number is half of the bottom number in the fraction.

Once the half is renamed as two quarters ($\tfrac{2}{4}$) it (obviously) has the same name as the quarter and adding is allowed, following the same rule: add the top numbers, the bottom numbers remain the same.

$$\tfrac{1}{4} + \tfrac{2}{4} = \tfrac{3}{4}$$

Again, if you say this in words it helps the addition make sense . . . 'Two quarters plus one quarter make three quarters.'

The same procedures and rules apply to subtractions with fractions. For example:

$$\tfrac{1}{2} - \tfrac{1}{4} = \tfrac{1}{4}$$

Again, to subtract a quarter from a half, the half has to be converted to quarters:

$$\tfrac{1}{2} = \tfrac{2}{4}$$

Once this is done, the subtraction can take place:

$$\tfrac{2}{4} - \tfrac{1}{4} = \tfrac{1}{4}$$

How to change the bottom number of fractions . . . 'renaming'
When $\tfrac{1}{2}$ is changed to $\tfrac{2}{4}$, you have renamed the fraction from half to quarter.

If you compare these two forms of a half with your number relationships 'hat' on, you can see that the top number (1) of the half has been doubled (×2) and that the bottom number (2) of the half has also been doubled (×2).

This sets up the rule for renaming fractions:

To rename a fraction, the top and bottom numbers of the fraction are multiplied by the same number.

For example: rename $\tfrac{2}{3}$ as twelfths.

The fraction is presently 'thirds'. To make 3 into 12, you

multiply by 4. This means you must multiply both numbers in $\frac{2}{3}$, the 2 and the 3, by 4:

$$\tfrac{2}{3} \times \tfrac{4}{4} = \tfrac{8}{12}$$

Another example: rename $\frac{3}{5}$ as twenty-fifths.

The fraction is presently 'fifths', so 5 must be multiplied by 5 to make 25. This means you must multiply both top and bottom numbers in $\frac{3}{5}$ by 5:

$$\tfrac{3}{5} \times \tfrac{5}{5} = \tfrac{15}{25}$$

Explanation

Renaming a fraction in this way does not change its value. $\frac{1}{2}$ and $\frac{2}{4}$ are both versions of a half. $\frac{1}{3}$ and $\frac{3}{9}$ are both versions of a third.

The explanation for this rests with the multiplication.

In the first example, the fraction $\frac{2}{3}$ was multiplied by $\frac{4}{4}$. In the second example, the fraction $\frac{3}{5}$ was multiplied by $\frac{5}{5}$. Both $\frac{4}{4}$ and $\frac{5}{5}$ are fractions whose value is 1. When a number is multiplied by 1 its value remains the same. The key to renaming fractions is to multiply top and bottom numbers by the *same number*, so that the fraction is multiplied by a fraction version of 1.

Other examples:

$$\tfrac{1}{2} \times \tfrac{6}{6} = \tfrac{6}{12}$$
$$\tfrac{1}{2} \times \tfrac{50}{50} = \tfrac{50}{100}$$
$$\tfrac{1}{2} \times \tfrac{30}{30} = \tfrac{30}{60}$$
$$\tfrac{3}{10} \times \tfrac{12}{12} = \tfrac{36}{120}$$

Procedures for adding and subtracting fractions

I sort the addition and subtraction of fractions into three types. I give the types very unmathematical names, but they are names that help me remember what procedure to use. Your first reaction should be to look at the bottom numbers of each fraction in the sum.

Type I: 'Samebottoms'

Adding and subtracting fractions which have the same name,

that is the same bottom number, is relatively easy. You apply the Golden Rules of fractions. *You only add or subtract the top numbers, the bottom numbers stay as they are.*

Examples: $\frac{3}{5} - \frac{1}{5} = \frac{2}{5}$
$\frac{3}{7} + \frac{2}{7} = \frac{5}{7}$
$\frac{8}{11} + \frac{5}{11} = \frac{13}{11}$

Type II: 'Guzintas'
A type II addition or subtraction is called a 'Guzinta'. An example will start the explanation:

$$\frac{2}{5} + \frac{3}{10}$$

When adding or subtracting fractions, remember that you must first focus on the bottom numbers. In this example these are 5 and 10. The 5 is a factor of 10. (A factor is a number which divides exactly into another number.) Here, 5 divides into 10 exactly 2 times. In less mathematical language, '5 goes into 10', hence 'guzinta'.

If the bottom numbers of the fractions are not the same, as in type II questions, one of the fractions has to be renamed. You rename the fraction that does the guzinta. Since 5 guzinta 10, rename the 5.

Renaming requires you to multiply the top and bottom numbers of the fraction by the same number.

For a guzinta fraction, you find this multiplying number by finding the 'guzinta factor'. In this example it is 2, because 5 guzinta 10 twice, that is 2 times.

Rename the $\frac{2}{5}$ using the guzinta factor:

$$\frac{2}{5} \times \frac{2}{2} = \frac{4}{10}$$

Now the two fractions have the same name (tenths) and can be added:

$$\frac{4}{10} + \frac{3}{10} = \frac{7}{10}$$

Another example:

$$\frac{5}{12} - \frac{1}{3}$$

Look at the bottom numbers, which are 3 and 12. The 3 'guzinta' 12 to give a guzinta factor of 4. The 3 is the guzinta number and $\frac{1}{3}$ has to be renamed by multiplying by $\frac{4}{4}$.

$$\tfrac{1}{3} \times \tfrac{4}{4} = \tfrac{4}{12}$$

Now you can do the subtraction:

$$\tfrac{5}{12} - \tfrac{4}{12} = \tfrac{1}{12}$$

Type III: 'Duzuntguzinta
Again, you look at the bottom numbers of the fractions involved. For type III these numbers are not the same and neither number is a factor of the other. For example:

$$\tfrac{3}{5} + \tfrac{1}{4}$$

or:

$$\tfrac{2}{3} - \tfrac{3}{10}$$

This type requires both fractions to be renamed. The only problem is to know what factors to use to rename each fraction. This is not a problem. The factors used to rename are actually within the fractions themselves.

For example, with the $\frac{3}{5} + \frac{1}{4}$ example, start by focusing on the bottom numbers, in this case 5 and 4. You use the 4 of the second fraction to rename the fifths which are the first fraction:

$$\tfrac{3}{5} + \tfrac{1}{4}$$

$$\tfrac{3}{5} \times \tfrac{4}{4} = \tfrac{12}{20}$$

You use the 5 of the first fraction to rename the fourths of the second fraction:

$$\tfrac{3}{5} + \tfrac{1}{4}$$

$$\tfrac{1}{4} \times \tfrac{5}{5} = \tfrac{5}{20}$$

Now that the fractions have the same name, the same bottom number, they can be added:

$$\tfrac{12}{20} + \tfrac{5}{20} = \tfrac{17}{20}$$

Now the $\frac{2}{3} - \frac{3}{10}$ example. The bottom numbers are 3 and 10, so you use the 10 as the renaming factor for the $\frac{2}{3}$:

$$\frac{2}{3} \times \frac{10}{10} = \frac{20}{30}$$

Use the 3 as the renaming factor for the $\frac{3}{10}$:

$$\frac{3}{10} \times \frac{3}{3} = \frac{9}{30}$$

The $\frac{2}{3}$ has been renamed as $\frac{20}{30}$ and the $\frac{3}{10}$ has been renamed as $\frac{9}{30}$. Now that both fractions have the same name, the same bottom number, they can be subtracted in the same way as Type I fractions:

$$\frac{20}{30} - \frac{9}{30} = \frac{11}{30}$$

To make Type III fractions have the same bottom numbers we are using the maths concept we used when working with times tables. This concept is the one which says that multiplying number A by number B gives the same answer as multiplying number B by number A.

For example, for the $\frac{2}{3}$ and $\frac{3}{10}$ above, the bottom number of $\frac{2}{3}$, the three, was multiplied by ten:

$$3 \times 10 = 30$$

and the bottom number of $\frac{3}{10}$, the ten, was multiplied by three:

$$10 \times 3 = 30$$

Both these multiplications gave the same answer, 30.

The principle behind Type II and Type III additions and subtractions is to rename one or both of the fractions so that you are dealing with fractions which have the same bottom numbers—that is, Type I fraction sums.

6   Decimals

All the numbers below are decimals:

12.5   66.9   0.95   3.25   and even   £25.95

Decimal fractions are another way of writing numbers less than one. In each of the examples above, the figures written after the decimal point (the dot) represent numbers less than one, for example the .5 in 12.5 represents a half. The identifying characteristic is the point, called the 'decimal point'. This decimal point separates the whole numbers from the part numbers:

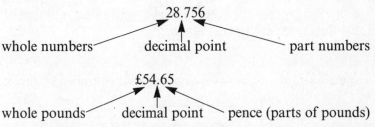

28.756

whole numbers   decimal point   part numbers

£54.65

whole pounds   decimal point   pence (parts of pounds)

Although decimal fractions are like ordinary fractions in representing numbers less than one, they are more specialist (or restricted). Decimal fractions only use tenths ($\frac{1}{10}$), hundredths ($\frac{1}{100}$), thousandths ($\frac{1}{1000}$), etc. Like whole numbers (which work on tens, hundreds, thousands, etc.), decimal fractions use place value (see p.22). The place that a figure holds in the decimal fraction dictates its value. Basically, the place of a figure in the number tells you whether the fraction is tenths, hundredths, thousandths and so on.

The order is logical. Decimal fractions become ten times smaller with each single move right from the decimal point:

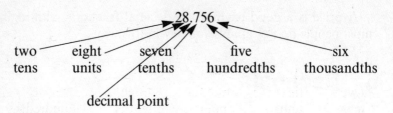

MONEY

Money is an everyday example of decimals. Sometimes a dash is used instead of the decimal point, but the principle is the same. The pound is the one unit, one whole. Pence are hundredths (since 100 pence are the same as £1) and each ten pence is a tenth (since 10 ten pences are the same as £1).

£9.99

£4−50

A price is a good example of decimal fractions, although most people do not analyse money in this way.

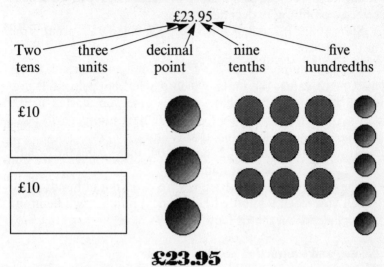

£23.95

| Two tens | three units | decimal point | nine tenths | five hundredths |

£23.95

The decimal part of £23.95, that is .95, is shown as 9 ten pence coins and 5 one pence coins. It could also be thought of using just one pence coins, which are each $\frac{1}{100}$ of £1. So .95 could also be shown as 95 one pence coins.

The .95 is $\frac{95}{100}$ of £1, or $\frac{9}{10}$ plus $\frac{5}{100}$ of £1.

Money is useful to show the connection between key fractions and key decimals.

fractions	money	decimal
1	£1 = £1.00	1.00
$\frac{1}{2}$	50p = £0.50	0.50
$\frac{1}{4}$	25p = £0.25	0.25
$\frac{1}{5}$	20p = £0.20	0.20
$\frac{1}{10}$	10p = £0.10	0.10
$\frac{1}{100}$	1p = £0.01	0.01

COUNTING IN DECIMALS

It can help your understanding of decimals if you do a little selected counting in decimals.

Start at 0.1, 0.2, 0.3, 0.4, 0.5, 0.6, 0.7, 0.8, 0.9 . . . what is the next number?

The next number is 1.0 (*not* 0.10). You have moved into the next place value, the units, which is what happens after you reach nine in a place value. In this case you started in the tenths. When you reach 9 tenths, the next number will be in the next bigger place value, that is units.

Now start at 0.01, 0.02, 0.03, 0.04, 0.05, 0.06, 0.07, 0.08, 0.09 . . . what is the next number?

The next number is 0.10. You are counting in hundredths. When you reach 9 hundredths, the next number will be in the next place value, that is tenths.

Adding and subtracting decimal numbers

The first step with adding or subtracting decimal numbers is to line up the decimal point. For example, with a sum such as:

$$12.3 + 3.219 + 4.35$$

the lining up gives:

$$
\begin{array}{r}
12.3 \\
3.219 \\
\underline{4.35} \\
\underline{19.869}
\end{array}
$$

This makes sure that you line up numbers with the same place values. In the example chosen, the 3 in 12.3 is 3 tenths, the 2 in 3.219 is 2 tenths and the 3 in 4.35 is 3 tenths, so these are all lined up to make sure you add like to like.

This also applies to money. For example, £12 plus £3.50 is added as:

$$
\begin{array}{r}
£12.00 \\
\underline{£\ 3.50} \\
\underline{£15.50}
\end{array}
$$

The most common mistake when adding decimal numbers is to line them up as though they were whole numbers, so 15.4 + 3 is added as:

$$\begin{array}{r} 15.4 \\ \underline{3} \\ 15.7 \end{array}$$ which is WRONG.

Multiplying by decimal numbers

$$15 \times 0.2 = 3$$

When you multiply by a decimal number which is less than one, the answer will be smaller, just as in fraction work. So in the example above 15 becomes 3.0.

There is a rule to help you place the decimal point in the correct place in the answer. First multiply the numbers as though there were no decimal point:

$$15 \times 2 = 30$$

Now look at the numbers on the fraction side of the decimal point. In this case there is one number in 0.2, the 2. The decimal point in the answer is placed this one number in from the right:

$$3.0$$

to give an answer of 3.0.

In the sum 1.2×0.6, first multiply the numbers, without using any decimals:

$$12 \times 6 = 72$$

Now count the 'decimal' numbers. There are two, the 2 in 1.2 and the 6 in 0.6, so the decimal point goes in after two numbers from the right:

$$.72$$

to give an answer of 0.72.

It can help to check against basic estimation guidelines:

If the multiplier is less than one, the answer will be smaller, for example: $7 \times 0.5 = 3.5$

If the multiplier is 1, the answer will be the same: $7 \times 1 = 7$

If the multiplier is bigger than one, the answer will be bigger: $7 \times 3 = 21$

SHOPPING

The favourite decimals used in shops are 0.90, 0.99 and 0.95. Think how many times you have seen prices like £4.99, £19.95 and (under £100!) £99.99.

It really is a great trick, and a fairly international one at that. Shoppers see £14.99 and focus on it as fourteen pounds. The 99 pence is as much as the shop can add to £14 before it moves to £15. It has the benefit of shoppers seeing £14, yet paying virtually £15!

When you get to big items like cars and houses, this place value subterfuge is still used: cars at £9 950 and £12 985; houses at £39 950 and £79 500. A little knowledge of place value in numbers combined with realistic cynicism can be useful.

I feel that this pricing device is aimed (though I think shops do it unconsciously) at inchworms who tend not to scan along a number, but focus on the first figures. Also they see numbers exactly as written rather than rounded up or down to some more convenient value. I suspect grasshoppers are immune to this pricing strategy.

7 Measuring

MEASURING LENGTH IN METRIC UNITS

I am sure that most people would rather avoid fractions of any kind. This is one of the reasons why we have pence rather than 'one hundredths of a pound'. The metric system allows us to avoid fractions by using a prefix instead of a decimal point.

If £1 is the basic unit of money, then 1 metre is the basic unit of length. The metre is too long for some measurements, so we need prefixes as a way of dealing with fractions of a metre. (The metre is also too short for big measurements, so there are prefixes to cope with this, too, for example a kilometre, but more of that on p.92.)

The metric system is based on ten and powers of ten (10, 100, 1 000, etc.). The fraction prefixes used are, not surprisingly, decimal fractions ($\frac{1}{10}$, $\frac{1}{100}$, $\frac{1}{1000}$, etc.).

The metric system uses prefixes to avoid using a decimal point. They are *deci, d* (not used a lot), *centi, c* and *milli, m* (used the most).

The table shows how this is done for metres.

$\frac{1}{10}$ metre	0.1	metre	1 decimetre	1 dm	$\frac{1}{10}$ m
$\frac{1}{100}$ metre	0.01	metre	1 centimetre	1 cm	$\frac{1}{100}$ m
$\frac{1}{1000}$ metre	0.001	metre	1 millimetre	1 mm	$\frac{1}{1000}$ m

The prefixes are an alternative way of writing a fraction. Instead of writing $\frac{59}{100}$ metre or 0.59 metre, we write 59 cm. Instead of writing $\frac{734}{1000}$ metre, or 0.734 metre, we write 734 mm.

Builders and DIY stores are more likely to use mm rather than cm for fractions of a metre, for example:

20 mm   is $\frac{20}{1000}$ metre
100 mm   is $\frac{100}{1000}$ metre, which is $\frac{1}{10}$ metre
1500 mm is $\frac{1500}{1000}$ metre, which is 1.5 or $1\frac{1}{2}$ metre

Big distances
A metre is approximately one long stride, but it is still not a big distance in terms of, say, travelling from London to York. For these distances we use the kilometre. The prefix kilo, which has been added to metre, means 'one thousand of'. A kilometre is 1000 m.

MEASURING LENGTH IN IMPERIAL UNITS

The USA and sometimes the UK still use Imperial units. The relationship between the Imperial units is based on a variety of numbers including 12 and 3.

12 inches = 1 foot	1 inch can be written as 1 in or 1″
3 feet = 1 yard	1 foot can be written as 1 ft or 1′
36 inches = 1 yard	1 yard can be written as 1 yd.
1760 yards = 1 mile	
5280 feet = 1 mile	

If you are changing feet into inches, you have to multiply by 12—for example, 8 feet is 8 × 12 inches. You can use the same strategy you used to multiply by 3, 6 and 7 (p.40). Multiply in two steps, using 12 as 10 + 2:

First multiply by 10   8 × 10 = 80,
then multiply by 2   8 × 2 = 16.
Then add the two parts, 80 + 16 = 96.

A foot is about the length of an adult foot (with shoe) and a yard is about the length of a comfortable stride. These approximations make estimated measurements of, say, a room, easy. For those of us who grew up with Imperial units, such estimations are almost intuitive. I can glance at the timber in the DIY store and pick out the 'two by four', that is the 2 inches by 4 inches cross-section timber. For metric measurements, I have first to convert to Imperial and then select my timber. This is a good illustration of the power of the *first* learning experience—that is, what you first learn about something new is what you remember best.

Conversions from metric to Imperial lengths and vice versa are shown in the table below.

accurate	*estimate*
1 in = 2.54 cm	1 in = 2.5 (2½) cm
1 cm = 0.3937 in	1 cm = 0.4 in
1 ft = 30.48 cm	1 ft = 30 cm
1 yd = 0.9144 m	1 yd = 90 cm
1 m = 1.0904 yd	1 m = 1.1 yd
1 mile = 1.6093 km	1 mile = 1.6 km or use $\frac{8}{5}$ km
1 km = 0.6214 miles	1 km = 0.6 mile or use $\frac{5}{8}$ mile

The estimate values provide the easy way to convert between metric and Imperial units. They provide key values (a technique which we shall use for foreign currency conversions in chapter 11).

For example, to convert 240 km into miles.
The answer will be a smaller number (because miles are bigger than kilometres). The key (approximate) values are 10 km = 6 miles
 and 8 km = 5 miles
So choose the key value which best fits the numbers you have. For 240 km the 8 km = 5 miles is good.

Now develop the key value, using simple multiples, starting with 10.

$$80 \text{ km} = \;\; 50 \text{ miles}$$
$$160 \text{ km} = 100 \text{ miles}$$
$$240 \text{ km} = 150 \text{ miles}$$

(This can also be used for mph and kph conversions.)

To convert 60 inches into cm.
The answer will be a bigger number. They key value is developed from the estimate   1 inch = 2.5 cm
                                    10 inches = 25 cm

So   20 inches = 50 cm
       40 inches = 100 cm
       60 inches = 150 cm (which also tells us that 5 feet = 1.5 metres)

To convert 80 cm to inches, the key value is developed from 2.5 cm = 1 in.
So   10 cm = 4 in.

Now do simple multiples of this key value:

20 cm = 8 in
40 cm = 16 in
80 cm = 32 in

The relationship between yards and metres allows a different technique for conversion. 1 metre = 1.1 yards. So a metre is 10% more or $\frac{1}{10}$ more than a yard.

This means that to convert metres to yards, you simply add 10% or $\frac{1}{10}$.

For example, 6 metres in yards is 6 plus $\frac{1}{10}$ of 6, which is 6.6 yards.

MEASURING VOLUME IN METRIC UNITS

The basic unit of volume (sometimes called capacity) in the metric system is the litre, shortened to 1. A litre is quite a large volume (about $1\frac{3}{4}$ pints) so, again, prefixes are used to deal with smaller volumes. The prefixes in the metric system are always the same, d for deci, which is $\frac{1}{10}$; c for centi, which is $\frac{1}{100}$ and m for milli, which is $\frac{1}{1000}$. This gives decilitres, dl, centilitres, cl and millilitres, ml.

> A can of soft drink is usually 330 ml, 330/1000 litre, about $\frac{1}{3}$ litre.
> A bottle of whisky is usually 70 cl, $\frac{70}{100}$ litre.
> A bottle of wine is often 75 cl, $\frac{75}{100}$ litre, $\frac{3}{4}$ litre.
> A tin of gloss paint is 500 ml, 500/1000 litre, $\frac{1}{2}$ litre.
> A pint of milk is 568 ml, $\frac{568}{1000}$ litre, just over $\frac{1}{2}$ litre.

I have yet to spot the reason why manufacturers use centilitres for some liquids and millilitres for others.

MEASURING VOLUME IN IMPERIAL UNITS

There is a complication to be explained here. Although the units for volume have the same names in the USA and the UK, pints and gallons in the two countries have different volumes. This is best shown in a table of the values:

UK	USA
20 fluid ounces = 1 pint	16 fluid ounces = 1 pint
8 pints = 1 gallon	8 pints = 1 gallon
160 fluid ounces = 1 gallon	128 fluid ounces = 1 gallon

Since the US pint is smaller than the UK pint, then its gallon must also be smaller ($\frac{4}{5}$ or 80% smaller).

The next table shows the relationships between Imperial and metric units of volume:

UK

accurate	*estimate*
1 pint = 0.568 litres	1 pint = 0.6 litres
1 litre = 1.761 pints	1 litre = 1.75 pints ($1\frac{3}{4}$)
1 gallon = 4.544 litres	1 gallon = 4.5 litres
1 litre = 0.2205 gallons	1 litre = 0.22 gallons

USA

accurate	*estimate*
1 pint = 0.454 litres	1 pint = 0.5 litres ($\frac{1}{2}$)
1 litre = 2.203 pints	1 litre = 2.2 pints
1 gallon = 3.635 litres	1 gallon = 3.5 litres
1 litre = 0.2751 gallons	1 litre = 0.3 gallons

When using the estimate values to work out a conversion of units, it may be important to remember whether the answer is an over- or underestimate. For example, an American pint is less than a half-litre, so conversions will give an answer which is slightly smaller than the accurate conversion gives.

MEASURING WEIGHT (MASS) IN METRIC UNITS

The basic unit of weight in the metric system is a little different in that it already has a prefix, the kilogram or kg for short. The prefix means kilo or 1000 times. This means that the kilogram is 1000 grams (a gram weighs about the same as a drawing-pin). So, for weights less than a kilogram, instead of a prefix the gram, g, is used. One gram is $\frac{1}{1000}$ of a kilogram.

A bag of sugar weighs 1 kg.
A packet of butter weighs 250 g, $\frac{250}{1000}$ kg, $\frac{1}{4}$ kg.
A packet of fudge weighs 100 g, $\frac{100}{1000}$ kg, $\frac{1}{10}$ kg.

Big weights

Once again weight is a little different from other metric units. A thousand kilograms should be a Megagram, because the Mega prefix means 1 000 000, one million, which is one thousand thousands (hence a Megastar means someone pretty famous).

Just to add to this rather individual situation for weight, one thousand kilograms is actually called a tonne (not a ton, which is the Imperial equivalent, 2240 lb): 1000 kg is 1 tonne (1 ton and 1 tonne are actually very close in value).

MEASURING WEIGHT (MASS) IN IMPERIAL UNITS

The Imperial units for weight are summarised in the table below:

16 ounces (oz) = 1 pound (lb)
14 pounds   = 1 stone (a UK unit, not used in the USA)
112 pounds   = 1 hundredweight (cwt)
20 cwt   = 1 ton
2240 pounds = 1 ton

There are some tricky numbers involved in these relationships, particularly 14 pounds to one stone. However, having 16 ounces to the pound (which makes the American pint of 16 fluid ounces a more consistent value than the UK's 20 fluid-ounce pint) is useful for $\frac{1}{2}$ pound (8 oz) and $\frac{1}{4}$ pound (4 oz).

To deal with the pounds to stones and stones to pounds conversions, a chart of key values can be used (see also currency conversions in chapter 11):

stones	1	2	5	10	15	20
pounds	14	28	70	140	210	280

Conversions between metric and Imperial measures of weight can be based on the values in the table below. For most everyday conversions, the estimate values are adequate.

accurate	*estimate*
1 ounce (oz) = 28.35 g	1 ounce = 30 g
	(though 25 g is often used)
1 gram = 0.0353 ounces	1 gram = 0.04 ounces ($\frac{1}{40}$ oz)
1 pound (lb) = 0.4536 kg	1 pound = 0.45 kg
	(just less than $\frac{1}{2}$ kg)
1 kilogram = 2.205 lb	1 kilogram = 2.2 lb

A quick way to convert kilograms into pounds is to double the kilogram value and then add on one tenth of this doubled value. For example, 40 kg gets doubled to 80. Add on $\frac{1}{10}$ of 80, which is 8, to give 88 lb. The conversion gives 40 kg as 88 lb. This is similar to the strategy used for conversion of metres to yards.

To convert pounds to kilograms, halve the kilograms and subtract one tenth of this value. For example, 90 lb gets halved to 45. Subtract $\frac{1}{10}$ of 45, which is 4.5 to give 40.5 kg. This is the reverse procedure of the one used to convert kilograms to pounds.

To convert ounces to grams, the estimate of 25 g for 1 ounce will give a slightly low answer and the 30 g for 1 oz will give a slightly high answer. Since 25 is $\frac{1}{4}$ of one hundred, it gives 'nice' answers:

ounces:	1	2	4	8	12	16 (1 lb)
grams:	25	50	100	200	300	400 (accurately 454)

If you wanted a better conversion, then add $\frac{1}{10}$ to each value. For example, 8 oz is roughly 200 g. Add $\frac{1}{10}$ of this, which is 20 g, to get a more accurate conversion answer of 220 g.

8 Percentages

This is another way of dealing with parts of one. Like decimals, percentages avoid the use of two separate figures as used in fractions. Percentages also have the advantage of using the easy concept of the numbers 1 to 100.

The words per cent mean 'out of 100'. 'Per' means 'out of' and 'cent' means 100. So per cent, like decimal fractions, is really a special, restricted value (name) fraction. All percentages are hundredths, $\frac{1}{100}$. The symbol used to indicate a percentage is %.

Percentages have a particular advantage. It is quite difficult to compare the values of different fractions—for example, deciding which is bigger, $\frac{15}{32}$ or $\frac{34}{75}$. This task is easy with per cents. It is obvious which is bigger out of 53% and 55%, even though the values are close.

The ease with which percentages can be compared is useful when comparing interest rates on different savings accounts or interest rates on different credit cards. Weather forecasters use the easy comparability of percentages as a clear way to indicate how likely we are to get rain. A chance of rain of 80% suggests it would be wise to take a coat when you go out. A chance of rain of 10% suggests you might risk leaving the coat at home. (I always get that 10% of rain just when I absolutely must go to the shop, post, train or whatever!)

So, let's get the big picture . . .

100% is the whole. It is one. It is all of something.
This is used as an everyday saying. If someone asks you for 100% effort, they want *all* your effort (unlike football managers who seem to want 110% or more from their players). It follows, then, that:

50% is one half, $\frac{1}{2}$.
25% is one quarter, $\frac{1}{4}$.
$33\frac{1}{3}$% is one third, $\frac{1}{3}$.
10% is one tenth, $\frac{1}{10}$.
1% is one hundredth, $\frac{1}{100}$.

Once again, these numbers can be inter-related so that easy values can be extended to give access to harder numbers.

An example will show how these key percentage values can work:

Our local travel agent adds 1% to your holiday bill if you pay by credit card. What is the extra payable on a holiday costing £750?

1% is $\frac{1}{100}$, so to work out 1% divide by 100.

£750 ÷ 100 = £7.50.   The 1% surcharge is £7.50.

Another way to approach this percentage calculation is to interpret 1% as meaning 1 in every 100 (so 20% is 20 in every 100, 25% is 25 in every 100 and so on). This is known as a ratio/proportion type calculation which is described in more detail in chapter 11.

For the travel bill percentage, 1% of £750 is £1 in every £100. There are 7 and $\frac{1}{2}$ hundreds, so the surcharge must be seven and a half pounds, or £7.50.

You can use the key values of 1%, 10% and 50% to get other values and thus close approximations for many other per cent values. Once again you make use of the relationships between numbers, for example:

5% is half of 10%
So if you can work out 10% of a number, if you then half that 10%, you have the 5% value, as in:

£800 . . . 10% of £800 is one tenth of 800, that is 800 divided by 10.

£800 ÷ 10 = £80   £80 is 10% of £800,

so 5% of £800 must be half of this £80,
that is £80 ÷ 2 = £40.

2% is twice 1%

If you can work out 1% of a number, it is easy to double the
value to get 2%, as in:

£800 . . . 1% of £800 is one hundredth of 800, that is £800
divided by 100.

 £800 ÷ 100 = £8.   £8 is 1% of £800
 so 2% of £800 must be twice this £8,
 that is 2 × £8 = £16.

In much the same way, if you want to work out 20% you can
double the 10% value. This is a handy estimate for 17.5% VAT
calculations.

For example, estimate the VAT payable on a computer costing £950. VAT is 17.5%. We shall use an (over) estimate of
20%.

 10% of £950 is one tenth of £950, which is £950 divided by
   10.
 £950 ÷ 10 = £95, so 10% of £950 is £95.
 So 20% of £950 is 2 × £95 = £190.

The VAT payable on a £950 computer is a little less than £190
(the accurate VAT value is £166.25—see below for the way to
work this out).

*Do not think that percentages are restricted to values of 100%
or less. It is possible to have values over 100%. For example
200% is twice the value of the original.*

Once you have grasped these basic and key percentage values, you can then progress to combining them to make even
more percentage values easy to calculate.
For example, you can add 10% and 5% to get 15%,
              or you can add 25% and 50% to get 75%,
              or you can add 1% and 10% to get 11%.

The easy, key values open up a wide range of percentages to quick calculations, which are useful for checks on calculator results, or as estimates for tips, or VAT additions to bills and shopping prices.

You can work out exact VAT percentages by realising that the easy numbers that make up 17.5 are 10, 5 and 2.5, and that $10 \div 2 = 5$ and $5 \div 2 = 2.5$. For example:

What is the VAT payable on a builder's bill for £480?
Work out 10%, then half this to get 5%, then half that to get 2.5%, then add all three values together:

```
10% is £480 ÷ 10 = £48
5% is £48 ÷ 2    = £24
2.5% is £24 ÷ 2  = £12
Add                £84
```

17.5% of £480 is £84.

Have you ever thought about the percentage interest rates charged by some stores for hire purchase? Sometimes these hover around the 33% level, which is close to $\frac{1}{3}$. So a video camera costing £600 would attract about £200 interest in one year (if you paid nothing off).

10%. A special case

It is a recurring theme in this book that maths ideas keep reappearing, often in different disguises. 10% is a good example of this. The quick way to calculate 10% of something is to divide by 10. Being able to divide by 10 is a basic, easy and essential skill.

Reminding you how to divide by 10 . . .

When you divide a number by one it stays the same value and (with the exception of a special case used in fractions) looks the same.

10 is one ten. When you divide a number by ten (one ten) it looks virtually the same, but there is an important difference: the figures in the result are the same and in the same order, but

they now have different place values. For example:

$$1\ 234\ 567\ 890 \div 10 = 123\ 456\ 789$$

Each figure now has a place value worth $\frac{1}{10}$ of its previous value (for example, the 7 has moved from being 7000 to 700). This makes sense, since if you divide a number by 10, *all* parts of the number should get 10 times smaller!

This last example had a convenient 0 in the units place. If another figure was in the units place, then dividing by 10 would take the answer into decimals, for example:

$$98\ 765 \div 10 = 9\ 876.5$$

Again, the figures in the answer are the same and in the same order as the original number and, again, each figure in the answer now has a place value which is $\frac{1}{10}$ of its previous value. For example, the 9 was 90 000 and has become 9 000 and 5 units have become .5 (5 tenths). This is a good way to start the calculation. Focus on one number and make sure its place value goes down to $\frac{1}{10}$ of its previous place value. Then make sure that all the other figures are in the same order as the original number. This will make all these other figures also $\frac{1}{10}$ of their original value. AND don't forget that you will find the unit figures (other than 0) becoming decimal figures.

The same principle applies to dividing by 100, one hundred. This will take figures down two place values (there is a reminder built in to the numbers here: 10 has one 0 and the figures move one place; 100 has two 0s and the figures move two places). This two-place move makes sense if you start with a simple example, say $400 \div 100 = 4$. The 4 has moved down two place values.

In a harder division such as $456\ 700 \div 100 = 4567$, the same two-place value move has occurred. You can check by focusing on the hundreds figure, 7, which has become a units figure in the answer.

If the number to be divided doesn't have a convenient supply of zeros at the end, you will have an answer which moves into decimal place values:

$$456\ 789 \div 100 = 4567.89$$

Again if you focus on that hundreds figure, the 7, it has again moved to the units place value.

This pattern and these strategies apply to any division further into the 10s series—1000, 10 000, 100 000, 1 000 000 and so on. To check, focus on an obvious figure whenever possible. For example, when dividing by 1000s check that the thousands figure moves down to the units place (1000 is one thousand. 1000 has three zeros, hence a move of three place values).

Other percentage calculations

Type 1. These are questions which ask you to calculate an exact percentage of a number. For example:

What is 35% of £660?

If you chose to use a calculator for this problem, you would need to remember the maths meaning of the word 'of', as in 35% of £660. It means 'times' or 'multiply'.

So the calculator sequence is:

1   key in 660
2   key in ×
3   key in 35
4   key in %

The sequence follows the maths equation 660 × 35% = 231. The per cent (%) key divides by 100 and does the equal (=) key so that the answer comes straight up on the screen. It does two keys for the price of one!

The full maths formula for percentages requires you to know that 'of' means 'multiply' and that % means '$\frac{1}{100}$' or 'divide by 100'. So 35% of £660 translates into:

$$35 \times 660 \div 100$$

The answer is 231.

Another example of percentages, this one about VAT.

A builder's estimate for repairing a roof is £1220 + VAT. What is the total amount to pay?

There are two options here. One is to work out 17.5% (VAT rate) of £1220 and add this to £1220. The other is to work out 100 + 17.5 = 117.5% of £1220, which will take you straight to the total bill.

Let's try the second option.

Rephrase the question. What is 117.5% of £1220? The 'of' means multiply and % means divide by 100. The formula is:

$$£1220 \times 117.5 \div 100$$

On a calculator, the key sequence uses the % button, which automatically divides by 100:

1   key in 1220
2   key in ×
3   key in 117.5
4   key in %

Answer: £1433.50.

The same strategy can be used with discounts. For example:

A car dealer offers a special summer discount of 12% on a second-hand car priced at £6495. How much is the discount price?

A 12% discount means the new price will be 100% – 12%, that is 88% of the original price. The new price is 88% of £6495, so get the calculator and look out for an answer a little less than £6495 (for your estimate, work on 10% less).

1   key in 6495
2   key in × (for the 'of')
3   key in 88
4   key in %

The answer is £5715.60

Type 2. These are questions which ask you to calculate a percentage from two numbers. For example:

*A pupil scores 47 marks in an examination in which full marks
are 80. What is her percentage score?*

Often with a word problem (on any topic), it is a good idea
to read and then reword the question until it takes a form that
makes sense to you. For this question, you could rephrase the
pupil's score to be, *'47 out of 80'*. The words 'out of' make the
question a fraction, $\frac{47}{80}$, which means 47 divided by 80. To
make the fraction a percentage, multiply by 100:

$$\frac{47}{80} \times 100 = 58.75\%$$

Alternatively, once you have decided this is a $\frac{47}{80}$ question and
thus identified the question as a division, you can use the %
key on the calculator. There are four steps:

1   key in 47
2   key in ÷
3   key in 80
4   key in % (the % button automatically multiplies by 100)

*The sequence of keys in these percentage calculations follows
the formula, as for example with $\frac{47}{80} \times 100$.*

9 Probability

This is a version of fractions, decimals and percentages used by, among others, gamblers and insurance actuaries. It puts the possibility of any event or occurrence on a scale of 0 to 1. A probability of 0 is that the occurrence is impossible. A probability of 1 means that the occurrence is certain. Not surprisingly, therefore, a probability of $\frac{1}{2}$ (or 0.5) is a 'fifty-fifty' or evens chance, the most common example of which is tossing a coin and choosing heads or tails. Probabilities can also be expressed as fractions or percentages.

The probability line		
0	$\frac{1}{2}$	1
impossible	*evens*	*certain*
0	0.5	1
0	50%	100%

For horse racing, the bookies disguise the fractions (otherwise they would have no customers—well, maybe a few mathematicians!). A $\frac{1}{10}$ chance becomes 10 to 1. A more remote possibility of $\frac{1}{100}$ becomes 100 to 1.

The chance of winning the Lottery with one entry is around 14 million to 1 or $\frac{1}{14000000}$, which is a number very close to 0!

When probabilities are given as percentages, the usual 'translation' applies, so a probability of 1 becomes 100% and $\frac{1}{2}$ becomes 50%. Weather forecasters use percentages to indicate the relative probability of rain or snow. A 90% chance of rain means that rain is very likely. A 10% chance of snow means there will be little chance of building a snowman.

SPINNING A COIN

Probabilities are about the relationship between a *successful* outcome and *all* the possible outcomes. To help understand this, think about spinning a coin and calling 'Heads'.

A coin has two sides. If it is a 'fair' coin, the chance of getting a 'head' or a 'tail' will be the same. This means that there are two possible outcomes altogether. If the coin lands as 'heads', this would be the successful outcome. So you have 1 successful outcome and the number of all possible outcomes is 2 and the chance of getting a 'head' on each spin of the coin is 1 out of 2 or $\frac{1}{2}$.

I can write a generalised probability fraction as:

Probability = the number of successful outcomes
                     the number of all the outcomes

Let's apply this to throwing a six-sided die ('die' is singular for dice). Say you want to get a four. That means you have 1 successful outcome, a four. The die has six sides and six numbers, so there are six possible ways that the die can land. So all the possibilities are 6.

The probability of throwing a four =

$$\frac{\text{The number of successful outcomes}}{\text{The number of all possible outcomes}} = \frac{1}{6}$$

Now let's look at the probabilities in the stars. I like reading my astrological forecast, but there is a probability barrier preventing me from taking it too seriously. Let me explain.

Say the population of England is forty-eight million (an underestimate, but it's going to divide better). There are twelve star signs. If the birthdays of these forty-eight million people are evenly distributed through the year, then there are about 4 000 000, or four million, people sharing each star sign.

I draw three probability-related conclusions from this:
It is a certainty that all predictions for a star sign will be vague!
It is probable that at least one of these four million people with the same star sign will fulfil one of these vague predic-

tions ('exciting news about money will land on your door-mat').

I think it is a low probability that descriptions of typical Taureans (or whichever star sign) will fit all the four million Taureans in England (except, of course, the bits I agree with).

10   Interconverting Fractions, Decimals and Percentages

Sometimes you have to convert a fraction to a percentage or a fraction to a decimal or some other interchange between the three. Since decimals, percentages and fractions are all ways of representing quantities which are less than a whole number, it seems logical that they should be interlinked. They are.

The best way to understand the links is to remember how each is constructed. This may mean a re-read of the relevant chapters.

Once again, focus on some key values:

fraction	decimal	percentage
$\frac{1}{2}$	0.50	50
$\frac{1}{10}$	0.10	10
$\frac{1}{100}$	0.01	1

The decimal to percentage and the percentage to decimal links are the most obvious (well, to me they are!). The figures are the same, for example 0.50 and 50%. There is a little more involved with interchanges involving fractions, but these are not an insurmountable problem. First, look at using the key values to demonstrate how the translations are done.

$\frac{1}{2}$, 0.50 and 50% have the same value. If you understand the maths used in each of these representations of a half, it becomes quite obvious that they are the same. Look at the three interpretations of the maths code used here:

$\frac{1}{2}$ means $1 \div 2$ which calculates out as 0.5.

$\frac{1}{2}$ can also be written as $\frac{50}{100}$ (see p.73).
50% means $\frac{50}{100}$ (see p.100).
0.50 means 50 hundredths, which is $\frac{50}{100}$ (see p.88).

We can now extend these key values into other values by combining, or by developing through the procedures we have used in other chapters, for example, dividing by 2:

$$\frac{1}{2} \div 2 = \frac{1}{4} \qquad 0.50 \div 2 = 0.25$$

Now divide both the $\frac{1}{4}$ and 0.25 by 2:

$$\frac{1}{4} \div 2 = \frac{1}{8} \qquad 0.25 \div 2 = 0.125$$
$$\frac{1}{8} \text{ is } 0.125$$

We can extend facts by doubling:

$$10\% \text{ is } 0.10$$

double both:

$$10\% \times 2 = 20\% \qquad 0.10 \times 2 = 0.20$$
$$20\% \text{ is } 0.20$$

We can also extend values by combining them:

$$0.50 \text{ is } 50\%$$
$$0.25 \text{ is } 25\%$$

now combine these by addition:

$$0.75 \text{ is } 75\%$$

(If you are combining fractions you will have to remember the rules for adding and subtracting fractions, see pp.81–4.)

Interchanging by formulas
This relies on an understanding of the codes involved in fractions, decimals and percentages. Although the three are written differently, they all have the same basic idea.

Fractions include a division—for example, $\frac{1}{4}$ is $1 \div 4$. Decimals and percentages can be converted to fractions (hundredths), which means they then also include a division. For example:

0.25 is 25 hundredths, $\frac{25}{100}$, that is 25 ÷ 100, and
25% is 25 per cent, 25 out of 100, $\frac{25}{100}$, which is 25 ÷ 100.

The conversions are centred on division and multiplication:

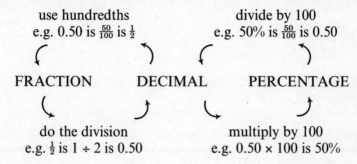

| use hundredths | | divide by 100 |
| e.g. 0.50 is $\frac{50}{100}$ is $\frac{1}{2}$ | | e.g. 50% is $\frac{50}{100}$ is 0.50 |

FRACTION   DECIMAL   PERCENTAGE

do the division   multiply by 100
e.g. $\frac{1}{2}$ is 1 ÷ 2 is 0.50   e.g. 0.50 × 100 is 50%

11 Proportion/ratio

Proportion (or ratio) is basically a division process, but with an extra step.

As a student I was forced by lack of finance, extreme hunger and flatmates who were the culinary equivalent of illiterate to learn how to cook for myself. For the first time I appreciated the use of proportion.

Later in my life I became a (mortgaged) house-owner. Again lack of finance, crumbling walls, muddy paths and friends who were the DIY equivalent of illiterate forced me to learn how to mix (and use) mortar and concrete. For the second time I appreciated the use of proportion.

Both these real-life examples of proportion take a rough (approximate) attitude to complete accuracy. But the principle you use is the same as with accurate proportion calculations.

Start with food. A simple recipe for a crumble topping is:

150 g flour
 75 g butter
 75 g sugar

150 g is twice 75 g, so the proportions (or ratio) are 2 parts of flour, 1 part of butter, 1 part of sugar, which makes a total of 4 parts (and 150 g + 75 g + 75 g = 300 g of crumble topping).

When dealing with proportion (or ratio) there are two numerical areas on which to focus:

the individual proportional parts; in this example, 2, 1 and 1.

the total number of proportional parts; in this example 2 + 1 + 1 = 4.

Although the recipe I used worked with 75 g, 75 g and 150 g, I could have used any values in the 1 to 1 to 2 proportions—say 1 kg of sugar, 1 kg of butter and 2 kg of flour (for a very large amount of crumble topping, 1 kg + 1 kg + 2 kg = 4 kg).

Now for the concrete experience of proportion (not to be confused with crumble mix, but similar in some respects).

The proportions (ratio) I used for mixing concrete were by volume, not weight. I interpreted one volume part as a heaped amount on a shovel, so for a dry mix of concrete the proportion parts are:

1 cement
2 sand
4 aggregate (chippings)

The total number of parts is 1 + 2 + 4 = 7.

So if it takes 35 heaped shovels to almost fill my wheelbarrow, I will need 35 ÷ 7 = 5 times each proportion part:

5 × 1 = 5 shovels of cement
5 × 2 = 10 shovels of sand
5 × 4 = 20 shovels of aggregate

To do this calculation, I needed to know the total number of proportion parts (in this example, 7). I divided the quantity I had to make (35) by this total number of parts to find out how many lots of each part was needed. I needed 35 ÷ 7 = 5 lots of each proportion part.

Now look at a 'reverse' example, where you have to divide something up into proportions. (Ordinary division divides things up into equal parts, but proportions are unequal parts. You have to add up the proportion parts before you do the division).

Say a lottery syndicate has five members—Mr Black, Mr White, Mr Orange, Mr Red and Mr Green. Each Saturday, Mr Black pays in £3, Mr White pays in £2, Mr Orange, Mr Red and Mr Green each pay in £1. They agree to share any winnings in the same proportion as their 'investments'. They win £4000.

The parts are 3, 2, 1, 1, 1
The total number of parts is $3 + 2 + 1 + 1 + 1 = 8$

£4000 has first to be divided up into 8 parts:

£4000 ÷ 8 = £500. So:

1 part is £500
2 parts are $2 \times £500 = £1000$
3 parts are $3 \times £500 = £1500$

To summarise (and check):

Mr Black	£1500
Mr White	£1000
Mr Orange	£500
Mr Red	£500
Mr Green	£500
Total	£4000

Three other everyday examples of proportion are maps, plans and architectural models. An artistic example would be a drawing (traditional rather than Picasso) of a human body. It would be obvious if, say, the legs were out of proportion to the rest of the body (except with Barbie dolls, but then they are not human) or if the eyes were drawn too high on the head.

Inverse proportion
So far we have looked at direct proportion—for example, if you were making crumble mix and you doubled the amount of flour, you would have to double the amounts of the other two ingredients as well. In direct proportion, if you halve one part you halve the other parts; if you multiply one part by ten, then you have to multiply the other parts by ten.

There is also an inverse proportion where, for example, doubling one quantity is balanced by halving the other quantity. For example, if you travel along a motorway for 120 miles at a constant 40 miles per hour, you will travel for 3

hours (and annoy a lot of people). If you then do the same
journey at twice the speed, 80 miles per hour, your travelling
time will be halved to 1½ hours.

If one bricklayer builds a wall in 12 hours, then, providing
they work at the same rate and keep out of each other's way,
three bricklayers will build the same size wall in 4 hours.
Using three times the number of bricklayers gets the job done
in one third of the time (in theory, but then much of the 'real-
life' maths in school textbooks is very much 'in theory').

If you look at this bricklayers example in terms of the numbers involved, you will see a constant value in multiplying the
number of bricklayers by the time taken to build the wall.

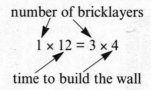

This is an example of the relative size (value) of the two multipliers for a given product—for example, if the product is 24,
the multipliers can be:

$$\mathbf{1} \times 24 = 24$$
$$\mathbf{2} \times 12 = 24$$
$$\mathbf{3} \times 8 = 24$$
$$\mathbf{4} \times 6 = 24$$
$$\mathbf{6} \times 4 = 24$$
$$\mathbf{8} \times 3 = 24$$
$$\mathbf{12} \times 2 = 24$$
$$\mathbf{24} \times 1 = 24$$

As the bold numbers get bigger, the ordinary numbers get cor-
respondingly smaller.

Foreign exchange and proportion
When you travel abroad you have to cope with a different currency with a different value. For example, in March 1998 £1
was equivalent to 9.925 French francs. (This is an easy rate of
exchange, being very close to 10 francs to £1.)

If you know the rate of exchange, then you can work out the cost of meals, shopping, hotels and so forth. This is vital for keeping to your budget.

There are accurate ways to calculate the exchange values, but you will need to have a calculator on hand. There are also good estimate ways, which are really a variation of proportion. And they can be a lot quicker than a calculator.

Let's look at the estimate method first, using some exchange rates which were current in spring 1998. Although these examples are specific, I shall try to build up a general method for you to use. The strategy uses proportions involving easy numbers.

HOLIDAY MONEY

Country	Currency	Rate per pound £1
Australia	Dollar	2.45
Belgium	Franc	61.1
France	Franc	9.88
Germany	Mark	2.96
Holland	Guilder	3.33
Mexico	Peso	14.2
Norway	Krone	12.3
Portugal	Escudo	300.4
Spain	Peseta	249.5
USA	Dollar	1.63

For example, the exchange rate for Holland is 3.33 guilders for £1. This can be made into numbers which are easier to use, since:

$$3 \times 3.33 = 9.99 \text{ guilders}$$

which is very close to 10 guilders, giving a reference exchange of £3 to 10 guilders.

So, the key proportion is £3 to 10 guilders and from this you can build up a mini-chart or table of exchange values:

guilders:	3.33	**10**	20	33.3	50	100	150	200	500	1000
pounds:	1	**3**	6	10	15	30	45	60	150	300

This table is a similar idea to the table used for long division (p.65). It uses patterns like 0, 100, 1000 and combines numbers to make new values (for example 100 + 50 = 150. You do not have to treat each exchange as a separate, unconnected calculation).

From these key exchanges you can work out others—for example, 120 guilders is 100 + 20 guilders which exchanges at £30 + £6, that is £36. This strategy combines proportion with building up and breaking down numbers.

The exchange rate for US dollars is £1 for $1.63. Again you have to find the easy numbers for a reference exchange rate. There are two possibilities:

> £3: 3 × $1.63 = $4.89, which is close to $5.
> or   £5: 5 × $1.63 = $8.15, which is close to $8.

A mini chart, combining these exchanges, would look like this:

US dollars:	5	**8**	10	15	20	50	100	150	200	500
pounds:	3	**5**	6	9	12	30	60	90	120	300

The exchange of $10 = £6 can be divided by 10 to give $1 = 60p

Spain has an exchange rate of 250 pesetas for £1, which is very easy at those values. Italy is 2938 lire for £1, which could be rounded to 3000 lire for £1 with acceptable accuracy.

Sweden's kronor is at 13.01 for £1, which comes close to easy numbers at £3 for 39.03 kronor, rounded to 40 kronor for £3:

kronor:	20	**40**	80	100	130	200	400	1000
pound:	1.50	**3**	6	7.50	10	15	30	75

Belgium's franc exchanges at 61.1 to the pound. To get to an easy key value, use £5 = 305.5, or 300 for easy calculations:

francs:	150	**300**	600	900	1200	1500
pound:	2.50	**5**	10	15	20	25

In all these tables, the in-between values can be estimated with good accuracy.

All you need in your pocket is a small card with the key value and some derived values and you can look like a mental arithmetic foreign exchange wizard.

I think we are conditioned to believe that we should be able to do whole calculations completely in our heads and that charts like these are soft options. We should learn to do what is effective for us. I would argue that for many people these little charts are more effective than calculators for quick estimations of currency values. They certainly provide sensible support for mental calculations.

12 Averages

Averages are often used in statistics, and since you should be very wary when interpreting statistics, you should also be very wary when interpreting averages.

First, what are averages and how are they calculated?

An average is usually taken to mean something in the middle or something typical, like an average family (I selected this example to sow the first seeds of caution in your mind).

There are, in fact, three averages in common use. The most common of these is the arithmetic average (also called the *mean* value). To calculate the arithmetic average you add up all the values and then divide by the number of values you added up.

This can be written as a formula:

$$\text{Arithmetic average} = \frac{\text{The sum of all values}}{\text{The number of values added}}$$

For example:

In one week in February, the temperatures each day were 12°C, 10°C, 9°C, 6°C, 4°C, 3°C and 5°C. What was the average temperature for the week?

The sum of all the temperatures is: $12 + 10 + 9 + 6 + 4 + 3 + 5 = 49$.
The number of values added is 7.
Average $= \frac{49}{7} = 7°C$.

This is quite a sensible average. All the values were reasonably similar, so the average was a middle example with not too much of a spread of values (called the range) each side. It doesn't always work that way:

The salaries of five men in a factory are £10 000, £12 000,
£8 000, £15 000 and £200 000. What is the average salary at
the factory?

The sum of all the salaries is:
£10 000 + £12 000 + £8 000 + £15 000 + £200 000 =
£245 000.
The number of salaries is 5.

The average salary is $\dfrac{£245\ 000}{5}$ = £49 000.

The average has been distorted by the one large salary. If the
range of values were quoted as well as the average, this would
help to make the picture a little clearer. The range is £220 000
– £8 000 = £212 000.

Another less than typical average value is average speed:

A family set off in their car to make a 120-mile journey,
mostly along the A38. The journey takes 3 hours. What is the
average speed?

Average speed is calculated by dividing the distance
travelled by the time taken:

$$\text{average speed} = \frac{\text{distance travelled}}{\text{time taken to travel}}$$

Put into the equation (formula) the values from the question:

$$\text{average speed} = \frac{120 \text{ miles}}{3 \text{ hours}} = 40 \text{ mph}$$

If you think about a car journey on non-motorway roads,
speed is not constant, the cars stop for traffic lights, slow up
behind tractors. Children may need to stop for toilets or a
drink. The average speed gives only very basic information
about the journey.

Treat averages cautiously. They can only tell you some of
the information needed towards the whole picture.

50% is used to indicate the middle value, the average. I often think education officials will only be satisfied with teachers when all children are above average!

13   Angles

The most familiar angle is 90°. It is in such common use that it has a name, the right angle, as well as a value:

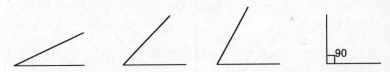

Unfortunately key angles do not use the easiest numbers. As I have just said, a right angle is 90° (when 100° would have been easier to work with numerically). A complete circle is 360°. You have to keep this difference from the tens system of 1, 10, 1000 and so on in your mind when you see work involving angles, almost as though they are issued with a health warning.

Some people's understanding of angles is blurred because they do not realise that when two lines meet at an angle, the angle size is not dependent on the length of either line (see figure below). The length of the meeting lines does not affect the value of any angle:

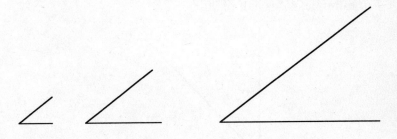

A right angle is a quarter of a circle. If you turn through four right angles (4 × 90° = 360°), then you have turned through 360°, which is a complete circle:

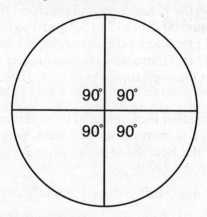

The U turn, immortalised by politicians, is a turn through 180°, or two right angles:

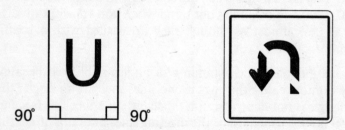

The right angle provides your key reference for other angles. For example, 45° is half of 90°:

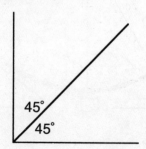

A clock can help you picture 30°. The circular face of a clock means that the second, minute and hour hand all turn through 360° every time they go round the clock.

If you focus on the 12 hours around the clock, then the hour hand turns through 90° from 12 to 3, from 3 to 6, from 6 to 9 and from 9 to 12 (and any other consecutive 3-hour time). If we pick on the 12 to 3 move, which is one quarter of the clock, it is obvious that the angle turned is 90°, one quarter of a complete turn.

This must mean that the hour hand turns through one third of 90° every time it moves from one hour to the next. For example, when the hour hand turns from 2 to 3, it moves through 30° (one third of 90°).

There is a 30° angle between every hour figure:

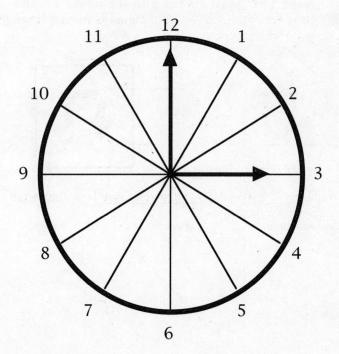

The three angles inside a triangle always add up to 180°
A triangle has three angles. The three angles inside any triangle add up to make 180°, no matter what the separate angle values may be. Try it by cutting up a triangle and putting the three angles together as shown. It will always be 180° (or two right angles):

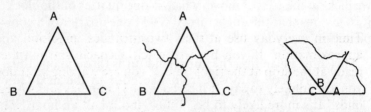

Teaching has taught me that certainty is a bold stance. I think that is why statements like 'the three angles in *any* triangle add up to make 180°' fascinate me with the power of their certainty.

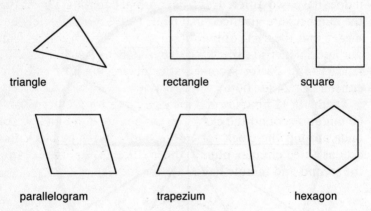

triangle   rectangle   square

parallelogram   trapezium   hexagon

14 Time and Clocks

Time in everyday use attracts two attitudes, precision and approximation. If you have to catch a coach you must be ready at the stop at the right time. If you are walking your dog you are unlikely to say, 'I'll be back in 33 minutes and 47 seconds.' It's more likely to be, 'I'll be about half an hour.' The demands for a precise use of time are less frequent in everyday life, so we have less practice and we tend, therefore, to be less skilled at this aspect of time.

Although time uses the figures 0, 1, 2, 3, 4, 5, 6, 7, 8 and 9, it does have two differences from normal counting. One is that the numbers are arranged in a circle (rather than a line). This means that the cycle of numbers repeats. Also, it differs from our normal metric-experience (based on ten) system because it repeats after 60 for seconds, after 60 for minutes and after either 12 or 24 for hours.

There are 12 hours round the clock face for the hour hand, 60 minutes around the clock for the minute hand and 60 seconds around the clock for the second hand. The clock face acts as three circular number lines (though the numbers for the second and minute hands are the same).

When you count round a clock in hours, the sequence is 1, 2, 3, 4, 5, 6, 7, 8, 9, 10, 11, 12. Then, providing you are not working on a 24-hour clock, it all starts again. The same applies to minutes and seconds: when you get to 60 minutes or 60 seconds, you start again.

This leads to a modification compared to the way you add ordinary numbers when adding seconds, minutes and hours. The modification requires an awareness of the number patterns for time and the appropriate adjustment to these 12, 24 and 60 number patterns.

Some examples:

40 minutes plus 30 minutes = 70 minutes, which is 60 minutes and 10 minutes, that is 1 hour and 10 minutes.

So 40 min + 30 min = 1 hr 10 min.

A 4-hour journey starts at 10 pm. What time does it finish?
This can be done as a two-stage problem, using 4 as 2 + 2. 10 + 2 takes you to 12 midnight. 12 midnight + 2 takes you to 2 am.

So the addition looks like 10 + 4 = 2, which, of course would be nonsense if the numbers were not using the circular 12 base of time.

A flight leaves at 20.00 and lands 8 hours later. What is its arrival time?
Using the circular system you followed above, 20.00 + 8 = 04.00.

This can also be done in two stages, going to 24.00 hours first:

20.00 + 4.00 = 24.00, then
24.00 + 4.00 = 04.00

Again, if you just looked at the raw addition, you might think someone was fooling around with maths. In the previous example you could see that 10 add 4 does not normally equal 2. The same is true of this example, 20 plus 8 does not normally equal 4. For number work with time you have to be very aware of the role of 12, 24 and 60 as 'start again' numbers.

This was an example of an additional complication for work with time—the twenty-four hour clock so beloved of train timetablers and travel agents.

There are 24 hours in a day, but under normal circumstances we work on two circuits of a 12-hour clock and use the letters a.m. and p.m. to indicate morning or afternoon and evening. So 7 a.m. is a morning time and 7 p.m. is an evening time. (The first is a breakfast time and the second is a cinema time.)

In theory the 24-hour clock should remove any confusion over the time of an aircraft flight or a train time. In theory!

Most people use the 12-hour system, so the 24-hour system is far less familiar. Times such as 15.35 do not trigger the same automatic response and understanding as 3.35 p.m.

As a traveller I am almost obsessive about times. I think one of my worse nightmares would be to arrive too late to catch my flight. So the translation from 24-hour times to 12-hour times is one I take very carefully, which means I double-check (usually twice!).

The translation is, of course, two-way, 24-hour times to 12-hour times and 12-hour times to 24-hour times. We tend to meet the first translation more often.

Translating 24-hour times to 12-hour times
In a day the hour hand of a clock travels twice around the 12-hour face of the clock. There are 24 hours in a day.

The first 12 hours 59 minutes generate the same numbers for both the 12-hour and 24-hour times since the first circuit of the clock face is the same for 12- and 24-hour times. So 8 a.m. is 08.00 hours, 11 a.m. is 11.00 hours and 12.45 p.m. is 12.45 hours.

At 1 p.m., the 12-hour time returns to the numbers 1 to 12, but the 24-hour time is now into its second circuit of the clock and 1 p.m. becomes 1 plus 12 (from the first circuit), that is 13.00. This continues, so that 2 p.m. becomes 2 plus 12, that is

14.00, 3 p.m. becomes 3 plus 12, that is 15.00, and so on.

Consider some comparisons/translations of key times:

	12-hour time	24-hour time
	12 midnight	00.00
	6 a.m.	06.00
	12 noon	12.00
	6 p.m.	18.00
and other examples:	7.30 a.m.	07.30
	4.15 p.m.	16.15
	10.30 p.m.	22.30

The times where mistakes are most likely to occur are the times from 1 p.m. to midnight. That is when the two systems become significantly different. So any 24-hour time between 13.00 and 24.00 could cause a problem. For example, a common mistake is to translate 20.00 as 10 p.m. (when it should be 8 p.m.).

To convert those 24-hour times which are in the 13.00 to midnight group into 12-hour times, the first step is to subtract 2 from 24-hour time to give you the key figure. All the resulting 12-hour times will be p.m.

For example, to translate 19.00 to 12-hour time, first subtract 2:

$$19.00 - 2 = 17.00$$

The 7 will be 7 p.m. when you have done the second subtraction, which is to take away 10 from 17.00:

$$17.00 - 10 = 7.00 \text{ p.m.}$$

As double checks, you could:
add back 12 to see if you return to 19.00, or
work back from 24.00 and 12 midnight, $24 - 19 = 5$ and $12 - 7 = 5$, or subtract 12 in one step, $19 - 12 = 7$.

Translating 12-hour times to 24-hour times
Again, if you can picture a clock with the hour hand moving

round for 24 hours, this should be straightforward. Up to 1.00 p.m., the numbers are the same. From 12 noon, the 24-hour time is on its second circuit, but instead of using the 1 to 12 numbers again (in conjunction with p.m.) the numbers carry on from 12 to be 13, 14, 15, 16, 17, 18, 19, 20, 21, 22, 23 and 24.

To translate the times from 1.00 p.m. to 12 midnight, simply add 12. Here are some examples:

2.40 p.m. becomes   2.40 + 12 = 14.40
7.15 p.m. becomes   7.15 + 12 = 19.15
10.30 p.m. becomes   10.30 + 12 = 22.30

15 Algebra

When you look at algebra in textbooks you notice that algebra uses letters as well as numbers. You have to learn some new codes in order to understand algebra, but after mastering these codes, algebra continues to build on the basic rules you learned for working with numbers. Algebra is useful as a form of generalising. This is a good reason for developing some understanding of the topic.

Most formulas are examples of algebra.

There are, then, some new conventions attached to algebra, some new codes to be aware of and learn. For example, algebra does not use a written × sign for multiply. There are probably several reasons for this. I think that one of the reasons is that mathematicians like to present information simply, in the sense of as little extra wordage as possible. (If you look at word problems in maths, none of them are heading for a Nobel prize in literature. Adjectives and adverbs are minimal and tend to be restricted to 'red' or 'fast').

An example of this reduction is the formula for the area of a rectangle (any rectangle). Starting with the word version:

Area of a rectangle = breadth times width

Now use A to represent area and b to represent breadth and w to represent width, so the formula begins to look like algebra:

$$A = b \times w$$

The times sign is not written in algebra:

$$A = bw$$

This formula can be used to give the area of any rectangle. It is a generalisation of the way areas of all rectangles are calculated. This formula suits mathematicians since it is a very succinct way of expressing information. Mathematicians use the word 'elegant' as their top approval rating of a piece of mathematical work. It is most likely that one of the characteristics of an elegant solution is its brevity.

Algebra does not use divide signs, something which you have met with fractions. This makes fractions a good example of how algebra represents division.

Fractions can be represented in algebra as:

$$\frac{a}{b}$$

This represents any fraction, providing you know that 'a' represents any number and that 'b' represents any number. It also means, as with fractions, a ÷ b.

Algebra can be a much clearer way of expressing an idea. Look at the next sentence.

I described an idea in chapter 3 which showed that if you multiply two numbers together you get the same answer whichever order you use for the multiplication—for example, $4 \times 5 = 20$ and $5 \times 4 = 20$.

A much shorter way of saying this in algebra is:

$$xy = yx$$

if x is one number and y is another number.

The equivalent idea in addition is:

$$x + y = y + x$$

These are simple, minimal presentation equations which put over an idea in a clear way, *providing you know the code*. Of course, this is why all subjects have their own vocabulary. Once you know the vocabulary, the code, a complex idea is communicated clearly. If a physicist is told something is a *transverse wave* she can immediately tell you a lot about that wave even before she knows its full identity. If you ask a guitarist to play an E chord, that is enough information for him to do that task. If you do not play the guitar you are lost without a quick lesson from someone who does.

Since algebra uses letters to replace some numbers, the letters must behave like numbers and follow the same rules as numbers (and vice versa). This interchange of numbers and letters can help you understand and work out algebra.

For example, let's make a formula for the perimeter of a triangle.

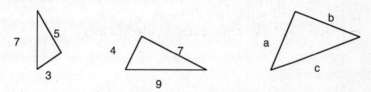

The perimeter means the distance round the figure, hence a *perimeter* fence. For the first triangle this is 3 + 5 + 7. For the second this is 4 + 7 + 9 and for the third the perimeter is, logically, the sum of the lengths of the three sides, a + b + c. This now can be used as a formula for the perimeter of any triangle:

$$p = a + b + c$$

where a, b and c are the lengths of the sides and p is the perimeter.

For an equilateral triangle, a triangle with three equal sides, each of length a, the perimeter, p is:

$$p = a + a + a$$

which can be written as:

$$p = 3a$$

This can be compared, but hopefully not confused with, the formula for the volume, V, of a cube which has sides each of length a:

$$V = a \times a \times a$$

That algebra code does not use the times signs, so the equation becomes:

$$V = aaa$$

which is written as:

$$V = a^3$$

Now, let's make a formula for exchanging pounds into US dollars at a travel agent's. This will introduce another item of algebra code, the bracket.

The exchange rate as I write this is $1.63 for £1. The travel agent will take a £3 commission fee for doing the exchange.

Start with a number example, say changing £103 into dollars.

Take off the commission: £103 – £3 = £100

Now work out how many dollars: 100 × 1.63 = $163

This was a two-step process:

1 take away the commission;
2 multiply the net amount in pounds by the exchange rate for pounds to dollars.

This can now be translated into algebra, using some code letters:

   c for commission;
   p for amount of money in pounds;
   d for amount of money in dollars;
   e for exchange rate of £ to $;
   and brackets ( ).

$$d = (p - c)e$$

This looks OK if you know the meaning of the brackets ( ), which are one of the algebra codes. Some of the codes tell you an instruction, for example + tells you to add. Brackets tell you two linked instructions.

Brackets hold items together, almost like putting them in a box. The brackets around p – c, (p – c), tell you to treat this combination of p and c together.

Brackets also tell you about the priority of using the operations add, subtract, divide and multiply. In building the equation:

$$d = (p - c)e$$

we subtracted (step 1) and then multiplied (step 2).

The rule or procedure of an algebra equation like this is DO THE BRACKET BIT FIRST.

The brackets also mean multiply. In much the same way as the code bw means b multiplied by w, $(p - c)e$ means $p - c$ multiplied by e.

So $(p - c)e$ tells you to:

1   do the inside of the bracket first, that is the subtraction $p - c$;
2   multiply the result of this subtraction by e.

Which is exactly the procedure we used for the £103 to dollars example. Algebra equations should always work when you use numbers in place of the letters.

This equation, $d = (p - c)e$, would work for any money exchanged with a commission subtracted. You would have to recode the letters—for example, to change pounds into French francs:

p is amount in pounds (the same as before);
d is the amount in French francs;
e is the exchange rate of £ to Ff.

The quadratic equation
This is a type of equation which is a top feature in early algebra. An example is:

$$A = (x + c)(y + b)$$

When you multiply the brackets out, the result is:

$$A = xy + bx + cy + cb$$

I shall try to show you how this is closely linked to the strate-

gies we have used for times table facts and for long multiplication. This should demonstrate once again how the same
ideas are recycled (in different disguises) time and again in
mathematics.

Let's analyse the equation $A = (x + c)(y + b)$.

It is one number, $(x + c)$ times another number $(y + b)$. For
example, remembering that letters represent numbers, x could
be 20 and c could be 3, so $(x + c)$ could be 23. In the same way,
y could be 40 and b could be 5, making $(y + b)$ as 45. So one
example of a number equivalent to:

$$(x + c)(y + b)$$

could be 23 × 45.

This is a multiplication which is the same as an expression
for area.

Now let's set up the area:

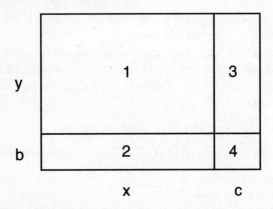

The are has four sub-areas, so the total area can be calculated
by working out the area of the four sub-areas and then adding
them together:

Area 1: xy
Area 2: bx
Area 3: cy
Area 4: cb

Total area: $A = xy + bx + cy + cb$

Try this again with another quadratic equation, this time a square:

$$A = (x + a)(x + a)$$

Area 1: x^2
Area 2: ax
Area 3: a^2
Area 4: ax
Total area: $A = x^2 + ax + ax + a^2$

The two ax combine to make 2ax, so the total area is:

$$A = x^2 + 2ax + a^2$$

16   Famous Formulas

A formula is a generalisation. For example, if I buy a bar of chocolate which costs 41p I spend 1 × 41p. If I buy two bars of this chocolate I spend 2 × 41p (82p). If I buy three bars, I spend 3 × 41p. This could become a little tedious, so I can generalise by using a formula which I can use to work out how much I spend if I buy any number of chocolate bars which cost 41p each:

'The amount I spend' = 'the number of chocolate bars I buy' times '41p'

This can be written in the algebra code. If I use S to mean 'the amount I spend' and n to mean 'the number of chocolate bars I buy', the formula becomes:

$$S = n \times 41$$

You now have to remember another piece of the code. The convention (normal practice) in maths formulas which use letters to represent the factors involved (in this case S and n) is not to write the times sign (×). This works on the principle that if it's not (written) there you assume it is there!

The formula becomes: $S = 41n$.

CIRCLES

If there is a scene in a film or play set in a classroom or lecture theatre, especially if it is a science or maths class, there will be a blackboard and written on it will probably be $A = \pi r^2$. This is the formula for the area of a circle (A), using r to represent the radius. π is a special value, a number which is a bit more than 3 and can be written to so many decimal places that this

activity can get the successful (and perseverant) person
(though really it should be their computer) into the *Guinness
Book of Records*.

This special number, which has its own symbol, π, is called
pi. Pi is to do with circles. It is a sort of Glastonbury number.
Natural, man.

If you want to try to find an approximate value for pi, take
a piece of string and wrap it once round a biggish tin can. This
length is called the circumference. Measure it. Now, as accurately as you can, measure the diameter of the can.

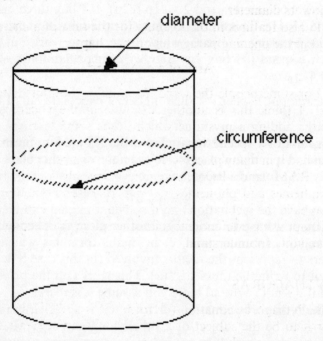

Divide the circumference by the diameter and the result
should be an approximate value for pi. A more accurate value
is 3.147.

Pi is the ratio of the circumference of a circle to its diameter, that is the circumference of a circle divided by its diameter:

$$\pi = \frac{C}{d}$$

You can turn this formula around to:

$$C = \pi d$$

so you can calculate the circumference of any circle if you know its diameter.

Pi also features in the formula for the area of a circle, as I said in the opening paragraph of this chapter:

$$\text{Area of a circle} = \pi r^2$$

For some people the word 'formula' is an immediate barrier. I think this is another example of the vocabulary of maths adding a mystique which keeps some learners away. This use of a special vocabulary is not unique to maths. You can find it in many places—for example, computer users speak of RAM and ROM, language specialists talk about graphemes and phonemes, car experts talk about torque. If you have the inclination and if someone explains these words without using even more specialist words in their explanation, then you can understand.

PYTHAGORAS

The Pythagoras equation (or formula) is sufficiently famous for it to be the subject of a rather long and somewhat contrived joke, which I am not telling here, involving a squaw and a hippopotamus.

Pythagoras was a Greek who lived about 2,500 years ago. He set up a secret religious society which explored the mysteries of number. He believed that the study of arithmetic was the way to perfection (something governments seem to believe when discussing numeracy).

Pythagoras was not the first to discover the theorem which

now bears his name. The Chinese used it for surveying and the Eygptians used it to help build the pyramids. This famous theorem has enabled builders to produce set-squares of exactly 90°. It has to be a pretty useful equation.

For a nation of such great architects as the ancient Greeks, an accurate measure of 90° would have been essential. A consequence of the Pythagoras theorem was the special case of a right-angled triangle, the 3, 4, 5 triangle. This is a triangle whose three sides are 3 units, 4 units and 5 units. If these sides are measured accurately and joined accurately, the resulting triangle includes an exact right-angle.

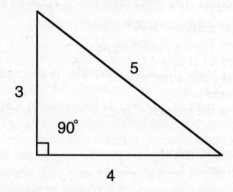

Pythagoras' equation deals with the lengths of the three sides of any right-angled triangle. If you square the lengths of the two smaller sides and add those two squares together, that gives the same number as the square of the length of the longest side. (This longest side, opposite the right angle, is called the hypotenuse): $a^2 + b^2 = c^2$.

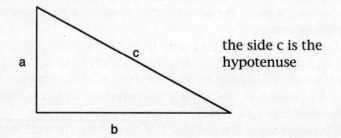

the side c is the hypotenuse

In the 3, 4, 5 triangle, the shorter sides are 3 and 4.

The square of 3 is 3 × 3, that is 9.
The square of 4 is 4 × 4, that is 16.
The sum of these two squares is 9 + 16 = 25.
The square of 5 is 5 × 5, that is 25.

For the practical construction of a right-angle, this 3, 4, 5 triangle is the simplest example of Pythagoras' equation. It is possible to have multiples of 3, 4 and 5 such as 6, 8 and 10 (where all three sides have been doubled).

The next whole-number example of this special equation is a little less practical. The three sides are 5, 12 and 13.

The two short sides are 5 and 12.
The square of 5 is 5 × 5, that is 25.
The square of 12 is 12 × 12, that is 144.
The sum of the two squares is 25 + 144, that is 169.
The longest side is 13.
The square of the longest side (the hypotenuse) is 13 × 13, that is 169.

It is fascinating to think that these calculations are thousands of years old. Number facts endure!

17 People Having Difficulties with Maths

There are many reasons why people fail to do well in mathematics. Usually there are ways to overcome or at least reduce their problems. Obviously not everyone is going to achieve, or want to achieve, a degree in maths, but mostly we should all be able to find a level of success which should meet our needs.

In this chapter I describe the problems of four learners. Perhaps there are some similarities to difficulties you have seen in someone you know, or even yourself. I have also included the reactions of Ann, a successful career woman who was suddenly faced with a mathematics section in her studies for a Master's degree ... a classic case of mathematics anxiety. Let's begin with her.

ANN

Ann is a 56-year-old grandmother, with a degree in social studies and a very successful career, who decided to take a Master's degree. Two years into the course she discovered she had to take a statistics module. She wrote to me for advice. She told me that at school she had been removed from maths classes at the age of 12 for being unteachable in this subject!

I sent her the WRAT* screening test, a basic maths test which allows a maximum of 15 minutes for your efforts. This is an extract from the letter she sent back with the test,

*The WRAT is the Wide Range Achievement Test, an American screening test for basic skills. I provided Ann with the maths part of the test.

perhaps the most moving letter I have ever received about difficulties with maths:

Dear Steve,

Thank you for sending the WRAT test. The few I managed to do in 15 minutes (I could not have done any more of the test even if you had given me 15 hours!) did not surprise me (even with the help of pen and paper). What did surprise me was the overwhelming sense of panic and deep sadness I felt as I tried to do it.

I sat at my own dining-room table, no noise, no pressure, and I felt like I was 10 years old again. I still feel shaken by my emotional response to this little test, I just felt I had to write to you straight away before the feelings fade. I just know that if I had been a 10-year-old boy doing the test while someone waited in the room, I would have torn it into pieces and run out of the room; I would have wanted to hit anyone who tried to stop me.

As it was I was taken right back to my parents' dining-room table 46 years ago when I was 10 years old, trying so hard to understand the homework to prepare me for the 11+ examinations. As I sat there as a 56-year-old mother, grandmother, qualified social worker, etc., the intense emotional response was overwhelming. I felt myself fighting back the tears, my hands starting to shake, my whole body tense. I just wanted to put my head down into my hands and sob. I found myself saying, 'I can't do it.' I felt an overwhelming sense of failure and despair.

I am writing this, not for sympathy, but because I am grateful to have gained an insight that I could not have otherwise achieved . . .

On a personal level, I feel quite proud of what I have achieved despite my learning deficit in respect of numbers. It may just be possible that I have achieved more because of the anger generated by feeling such a failure. Who knows? It really is not important for me any more. I suddenly feel that by chasing academic achievement all these years I have been trying to compensate for feeling stupid ('If I get A levels I can't be stupid; if I get a BA I can't be stupid; if I get an MA I can't be stupid', etc.) . . .

Ann's letter illustrates how the consequences of being unsuccessful in maths can affect many aspects of your life. Whilst she was spurred on, trying to compensate for this area of failure, others may just give in and confine themselves to the safe options in life.

Whilst researching aspects of mathematics for this book, I carried out informal assessments (that is, assessments which did not consist of standard tests alone) on several children who were having difficulties with maths. They were all very individual in their problems. There was, however, a common factor—a failure to learn all the times table facts.

I chose the word 'failure' in the last sentence very deliberately, because that is what it seemed to each of the children. One day, one day it will be understood that there are a number of children who, despite their very best efforts, cannot learn all the times table facts. I am not saying that children should not try, but I am saying that parents and/or teachers who persist in insisting that they must learn them, risk demotivating the child. Do not set a target that is out of reach of the child.

In any assessment of maths I rely heavily on the deeply significant and complex psychological question, 'How did you do that?' Sometimes I rephrase it to say, 'Can you tell me how you worked that out?', but it's a good strategy, especially if the person cannot guess what answer he or she thinks you want to hear. It certainly deals with any preconceived ideas I may be about to attribute to the person doing the work.

For example, I was working with a 15-year-old boy who was doing quite well in maths (he achieved a grade B in GCSE maths). I discovered that he calculated 3×6 by halving the answer to 6×6. 'Aha,' I say, leaping to a sweeping generalisation, 'I have noticed that many people who cannot remember all the times table facts, do know the square number facts.' James put me right. 'I know just the 6×6 fact because when I lost my two front teeth as a child, my speech therapist made me say six times six is thirty-six over and over again.'

LORNA

Lorna, aged 12, came to see me after her educational psychologist suggested her parents might like to seek a little more information on her maths difficulties. He had found her achievements in maths to be around three years behind expectations. Lorna's IQ was at the lower end of average, but she had good language skills. Her psychologist described her as having 'little faith in her own ability in maths, possibly comparing this unfavourably to her good skills in language.'

Lorna certainly had lost faith in herself and, understandably, took a little while to involve herself in the maths tasks I asked her to do. (The best way to learn about someone's maths abilities is to watch them doing some maths, preferably encouraging them to talk you through their procedures and thoughts.)

Lorna had good counting skills which were both accurate and quick. She did most of the counting in her head (some children use dots or tallies to keep tracks, others may finger-count). For 9 + 8 she added, by counting in her head, first 5 and then 3. She also answered quickly and accurately, using the same procedure, 9 + 6 (added 3 and 3) and 9 + 4 (added 2 and 2).

Although she used the same strategy again for ? + 8 = 14 and 9 + ? = 13, this different, slightly less familiar presentation, was answered more slowly.

Lorna said she could do most times tables, but 'didn't know the 9s'. In reality, she did not have immediate recall of these facts, she counted on. She was good at this, and was, for example, able to count on in 3s and 7s. I asked her, 'What are eight nines?' Lorna said she didn't know the nine times table (as she had already told me). I asked her if she could tell me the answer to nine eights, which she did by counting on in eights. She could count backwards accurately.

She was also able to adapt the familiar sequence 10, 20, 30,

40 . . . to a less familiar form: 12, 22, 32, 42 . . .

It was interesting to see someone who was so adept at sequencing with quite difficult numbers. Lorna obviously was not aware that 8 × 9 and 9 × 8 gave the same answer and she had not absorbed the pattern of adding 9, which is easier than the pattern of adding 8. I find examples of anomalies in skills in many people.

It is possible to extend the skills such people do have into new areas, because the groundwork is there. It just hasn't been developed to its fullest extent.

Lorna needs careful instruction on place value, possibly using base ten blocks. Again there were inconsistencies in levels of knowledge. For example she named 9026 as nine hundred and twenty six, but named 1205 as twelve hundred and five (easier to say than ninety hundred and twenty-six). She had little understanding of zero.

Lorna is an inchworm (see p.16). She also rushes her work, and a rushing inchworm with a poor knowledge of basic facts and procedures is in some mathematical danger!

If Lorna is not encouraged to develop her effective counting skills into more sophisticated maths skills her progress will be limited. The problem with moving someone away from an inefficient, but secure skill is that they are likely to resist and, when they do try, will probably do less well until the new skill is mastered.

Lorna had no concept of money. This is unfortunate on two counts. One is that money is a good teaching aid, and two is that knowing about money is a life skill.

This gap in her knowledge showed up in her answers to two decimal questions. She interpreted 12.3 + 5 as 12 + 3 + 5 and 63 + 2.1 as 63 + 2 + 1. Money is a good teaching aid for decimals. If you understand money.

There are certain priority targets to aim at if Lorna is to progress. I wrote of the maths wall being able to stand with some bricks missing (p.12). Lorna's maths wall needs some more bricks before it can support its present state and certainly before it can be built any higher. As ever, she has to be taught to build on what she knows and to be taught in the way that is sympathetic to the way she works (her inchworm cognitive style).

JILL

Jill was a fascinating example of a person with a specific difficulty in mathematics. She came to see me with her mother, who gave me an impressive pen picture of her daughter.

Jill was 14 years old. She was in the gifted group at her comprehensive school. She had taught herself to read when she was three and was now reading around twenty books a week. At fourteen she was teaching herself Hebrew and Sanskrit. She arrived in my office with a copy of Virgil, in Latin of course (which, without question, was the subject which gave me my most catastrophic failure are school).

Jill's mother felt that her daughter's early lessons in maths had been inappropriate. Also, Jill did not get the same positive feedback she received from her work in English and foreign languages.

Despite being in the gifted group at school, she was in the middle set for maths. Not surprisingly, when you think of the nature of the sciences, she liked biology more, and did better in it, than chemistry and physics.

Initially, Jill avoided answering any open-ended questions, but as she began to feel less threatened by the conversation she provided some clear observations of her own strengths and weaknesses in maths. She summed up her problems in maths as, 'I think I understand it, I write it down, but then I've missed something vital. Suddenly I can't remember things.' (This last statement from someone who can obviously remember several languages. Jill is an example of an individual with the specific memory blocks that seem to be related to maths.)

I scattered some poker chips on the table and asked her to estimate how many were there. She protected herself by saying, 'It's a wild guess,' and guessed 35. She accurately counted the 51 chips, without grouping them in tens or fives which would have allowed her to check the answer.

I like the task where I give ten one pence coins, five two

pence coins and two five pence coins and ask the person to show me as many ways as they can to make 9p, using the coins as many times as they wish. Jill showed that her sense of number values, even at this level, was poor and that she did not tackle this task logically.

On the WRAT Test (see p.151), this gifted girl scored at the 23rd percentile, that is 77 per cent of her age group would do better.

I asked Jill to give me an easier number, an estimate, for 882 (one of the numbers from a question on the WRAT test). She suggested 880. Taken with other observations, it seems that Jill has poor estimation skills and a poor concept of relations in numbers. This deficit in estimation skills does not support her cognitive (thinking) style.

I feel that an inclination towards a particular cognitive style is inherent, but the back-up skills you need to be successful with that style often need to be learnt (and therefore taught).

Jill needs to develop a sense of the values of numbers to enable her to maximise the potential value of her grasshopper style. This feeling about her was further supported by her answers to some questions which are designed to investigate cognitive style. One of my favourite questions for this is a chessboard-like square of 49 black and white little squares. The question is, 'How many black squares?' The answer is 25 (and thus 24 white). Inchworms often count the squares to get their answer, but grasshoppers just look at the picture and say '25 black'. Jill looked at the picture and said, 'It's either 24 or 25, I just can't make up my mind which.' She had that holistic ability to look and almost see an answer, but didn't quite have enough number skills to be sure.

Jill used strategies to compensate for her poor ability to recall basic facts. For example, she derived $9 + 8$ from $9 + 9 - 1$ and $9 + 6$ from $10 + 6 - 1$. She computed 8×5 from half of 8×10. This suggests that inchworm skills are not her natural inclination. Further support for this was her reluctance to write down any 'working'.

She had developed a fatalistic vagueness in her attitude to maths. I particularly liked her explanation of her error with:

$$\begin{array}{r} 391 \\ -88 \\ \hline 317 \end{array}$$

She looked at the units column where she had, incorrectly, taken 1 from 8 and said, 'I take away the number which is more comfortable without realising it.'

There is no doubt that Jill should be taught, as indeed should anyone, by methods which acknowledge her abilities, thinking style and weaknesses. She will not survive the sausage factory approach, where one of the (misguided) principles is, 'Do it this way.'

SAM

Sam was 10 years 6 months old when his mother brought him to see me. She felt that he was underachieving in maths.

He was a quiet boy, but very willing to get started on some maths, so we began with the WRAT arithmetic test. Sam worked with great perseverance for 12 minutes. He answered 14 items correctly and 14 incorrectly. He used dots as tally marks.

He avoided answering 7 × 6 and $\frac{15}{5}$ and made three multiplication fact errors within other questions.

In the informal part of the assessment procedure, Sam showed that he had good knowledge of basic addition facts to 10, but had difficulty with the addition facts beyond this. He attempted to count in his head for these facts. He said that he knew the times table facts for 2×, 3×, 5× and 10×, but finger-counted for 8 × 5 and worked from 4 × 3 to get an answer to 6 × 3. He knew that 8 × 7 and 7 × 8 give the same answer. He had problems with the times table tests at school because the answers were required too quickly.

Sam used dots to work out basic facts when doing written maths tasks, but tried to count in his head, that is without any props (like his tally dots), when asked to answer basic fact questions mentally. He had no compensatory strategies for the times table facts which he could not recall. These are major handicaps and are likely to be cumulative, that is they will have more and more significance as he moves on through the maths syllabus at school.

Sam had another familiar maths difficulty. His vocabulary for the basic operations of $+ - \times$ and $\div$ was limited. He also showed the contradictions that children often show in what they can and cannot do in maths. He answered $601 - 346$ incorrectly, yet answered quickly and accurately $19.01 + 10.91$.

Some teachers and parents assume that if a child can do a 'hard' maths question, then he or she can do all 'easy' questions. This logic, in my experience, does not apply to children learning maths.

Sam is an inchworm. He also has poor knowledge of basic facts, a poor short-term memory and poor estimation skills. These three problems have significant impact on inchworms, who need a good memory to cope with all the steps they have to use to answer a question. Having poor recall of basic facts adds a further load on the memory needed to work out answers, and poor estimation skills mean that they have no ability to appraise answers.

An awareness of how Sam does maths and what he finds difficult is essential for any teacher working with him.

HARRY

Harry was 12 years 7 months when his father asked me to look at his work in maths. The father was concerned about the level of Harry's maths performance as he approached common entrance examinations. The boy was in the upper sets for all subjects except maths and science.

Harry worked cheerfully and cooperatively throughout the assessment. (I am often amazed by how perseverant some children are despite the less than positive experience they have of maths.)

He showed some of the anomalies I have come to expect when I ask children to work through some maths questions.

For example, he used subtraction procedures accurately, except when a zero was involved.

There seems to be a widespread problem with understanding zero, particularly in subtractions. It could be that the idea of taking something away from nothing is just too far outside a child's perception of fairness to be a comfortable action.

Harry was able to convert $\frac{3}{4}$ to 75% and $\frac{3}{8}$ to 37.5% (perhaps he saw the link). He could work out 20% of 120, but incorrectly converted $52\frac{1}{2}$% to 52.5. He avoided the fraction questions.

He had quick recall of basic addition and subtraction facts to 20. He used strategies for some addition facts—for example, 7 + 8 was quickly calculated via 7 + 7. He did 9 + 8 via 10 + 8 and 14 – 8 was done in two steps as 14 – 4 = 10 and 10 – 4 = 6.

I asked Harry which times table facts he knew. He said he knew the times table facts 'OK, though I may not know them straight away.' When I asked which ones he did know straight away, Harry said the 2×, 5× and 10×. However, he knows and uses the commutative property (this is the transposal of numbers—for example, 3 × 4 to 4 × 3, which still gives the same answer, in this case, 12). He answered 3 × 8 via 2 × 8 plus 4 and 4.6 × 9 was done via 6 × 10 minus 6, and 7 × 6 was done as 6 × 6 plus 6.

He used quite sophisticated strategies. During this part of our session he said, 'I'm good at working things out in my mind, it's showing my working out that's the problem.'

He tackled the 9p task (p.156–7) systematically.

Harry showed distinctly grasshopper tendencies with the cognitive style questions I asked him to try. I looked at his exercise book from school. There was little doubt that his teacher was an inchworm and that he expected Harry to use those methods.

Harry does not like formulas and does not see any reason to use them, but he if he is to survive an inflexible regime of school maths he will need to learn how to use them. It will actually be of benefit to him to learn this skill, but he will need to be convinced of the benefits. At the moment, he has alternative ways of arriving at answers that are easy for him. He sees no reason to change to procedures which, in his view, are longer and more cumbersome.

He also needs to improve his skills with word problems.

One of the ways to encourage this skill is to teach children to take a number equation (like 12 + 5 = 17) and for them to make up their own word problem around these numbers. Initially, children tend to be very stilted (I have 12 pens, you have 5 pens. How many pens do we have altogether?). They can be led to far more creative and devious stories!

Harry has all the basic abilities for success in maths. Like so many children, he has not organised his skills to maximise their potential, nor has he recognised all the patterns and inter-relationships in maths. Although he does extend facts, he could be taught to be even more creative and effective with this ability. A potential problem is his grasshopper style which is preventing him from tackling formulas and could cause a breakdown in communication between teacher and child.

Appendix

Two words from the maths vocabulary used in this book
I have used the words 'figure' and 'number' quite specifically
to mean:

> *Figure* Any of the symbols 0, 1, 2, 3, 4, 5, 6, 7, 8, 9.
> *Number* Any of the figures, used individually or combined
> to represent a value. For example, 14 is fourteen, 506 is five
> hundred and six. (*See also place value*, p.22).

Other maths books by Steve Chinn
Mathematics for Dyslexics: A Teaching Handbook (with J. R.
 Ashcroft), 2nd ed., Whurr, 1998.
What to do when you can't learn the times tables, Egon, 1996.
What to do when you can't learn the times tables on CD-ROM.
 Available from Mark College, Mark, Somerset TA9 4NP,
 UK.
What to do when you can't add and subtract, Egon, 1998.